WELLNESS IN

Personal Wellness Solution

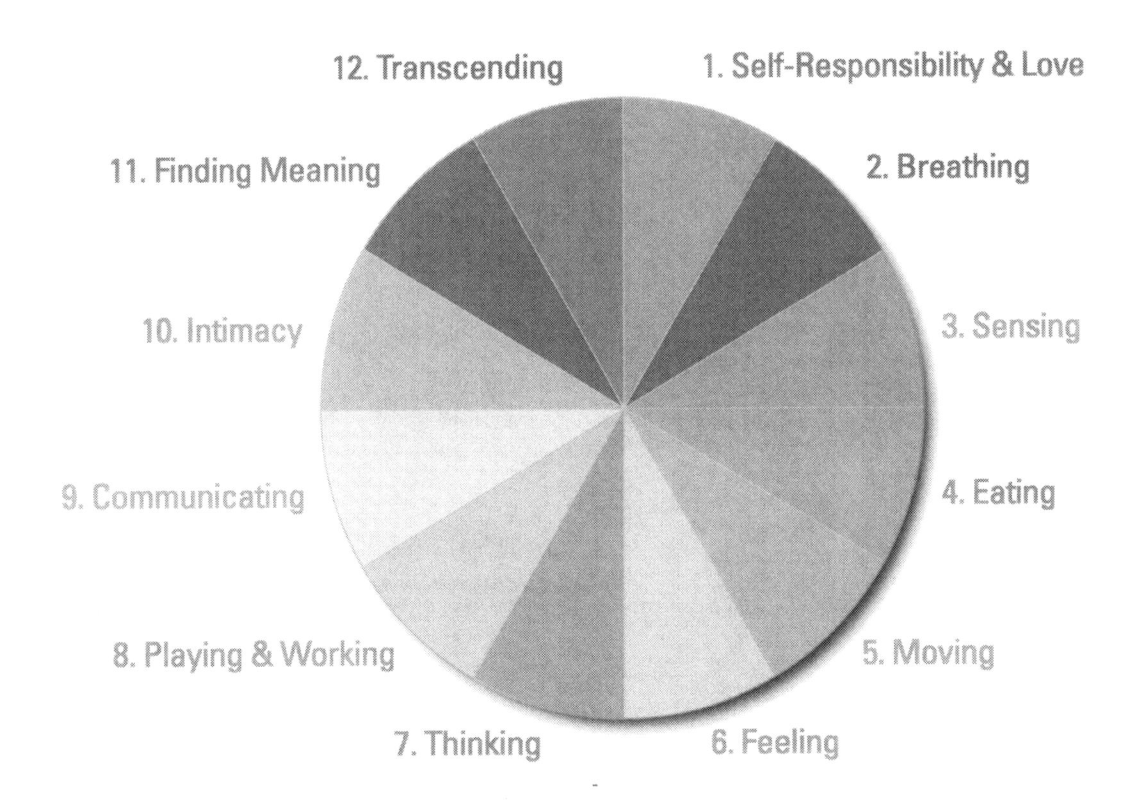

Whole Person Wellness Program

- Assess clients' level of wellbeing in 12 key dimensions.
- Discover key areas of motivation for change.
- Co-create personalized wellness action plans.
- Implement small steps for continuous improvement.
- Support a higher level of energy, health, and wellbeing.

www.WellPeople.com

Energy Psychology
Theory, Research, & Treatment

Journal of the National Institute for Integrative Healthcare (NIIH.org)

www.EnergyPsychologyJournal.org

Energy Psychology: Theory, Research, and Treatment is a peer-reviewed professional journal dedicated to reporting developments in the field of energy psychology (EP) that are of interest to health care professionals and researchers. It contains original empirical research into the efficacy of EP methods; theoretical, experimental, and basic science papers illuminating the mechanisms of action of EP; clinical insights on the application of EP to various populations, and interfaces with other interventions; book reviews, and abstracts published in other journals that are of relevance to the EP field. Its goal is to further the development of EP as an evidence-based method in the healing sciences. It conforms to the editorial, stylistic, and ethical standards of the American Psychological Association (APA.org).

Energy Psychology: Theory, Research, and Treatment (ISSN 1949-6575) is published biannually (November and May) by Energy Psychology Press, PO Box 442, Fulton, CA 95439. For customer service or advertising information, contact 707-237-6951 or energypsychologypress@gmail.com.

POSTMASTER: Send address changes to: *Energy Psychology* journal, PO Box 442, Fulton, CA 95439.

YEARLY SUBSCRIPTION RATES: $49.95 per issue, $99.95 per year.

AUTHOR ENQUIRIES: Submit paper copies of proposed papers to *Energy Psychology* journal, PO Box 442, Fulton, CA 95439. Include an e-mail address and phone number for the corresponding author. All submissions should conform fully to the requirements of the *Publication Manual of the American Psychological Association,* sixth edition. Include a cover letter as specified on the "Submissions" link at www.EnergyPsychologyJournal.org, and manuscripts should be prepared in conformity with the other standards published there. Acceptance or rejection will be made via e-mail; paper copies will not be returned. If a submission is accepted for peer review, all subsequent contact will occur via e-mail. Deadline for Spring issue submissions is Jan 15 of each year, and July 15 for Fall issue.

REPRINTS: Back issues are available for $49.95. Reprint ordering information may be found at www.EnergyPsychologyPress.com. To order 100 or more copies of a particular paper, contact energypsychologypress@gmail.com.

DISCLAIMERS:

No responsibility is assumed by the publisher or authors for any injury and/or damage to persons or property as a matter of product liability, negligence, or otherwise, or from any use or operation of any methods, products, instructions, or ideas contained in the material herein. No part of this publication is meant to offer medical or psychological advice for a particular individual or condition, or a group of individuals or conditions, and no person should use any information in this publication as a substitute for medical or psychological care. These methods should only be applied under the supervision of a licensed medical or psychological healthcare professional.

Advertising material in this journal is expected to conform to the ethical standards of the American Psychological Association, which may be found at apa.org. Inclusion in this publication does not constitute a guarantee or endorsement of the quality or value of any product or service advertised, or the claims made by the advertiser, by the publisher, or its employees or associates. No liability of any nature whatsoever is assumed, accepted, or implied by these parties by the inclusion of any the material in this journal. The opinions stated are those of the author(s), and do not necessarily represent the policies or views of the publisher, editors, and staff.

Contents

November 2014 • Volume 6, Number 2

About

ENERGY PSYCHOLOGY: THEORY, RESEARCH, AND TREATMENT

Energy psychology (EP) is an evolving and maturing field that is rapidly meeting the standards of proof for "evidence-based" practice. Studies of EP have demonstrated its efficacy for a wide range of psychological and physical problems, from phobias to pain to posttraumatic stress disorder. EP is now being researched in hospital systems such as Britain's National Health Service (NHS), large private hospital chains such as Kaiser Permanente and Sutter Health, and the United States Department of Veterans Affairs (VA). By providing a rigorous, high-quality, peer-reviewed platform for the publication of research results, theory, and clinical insights, this journal provides a forum for the exchange of the key discoveries and ideas that drive the EP field forward.

—Dawson Church, PhD
Editor, *Energy Psychology: Theory, Research, and Treatment*

The journal publishes work in the following areas:

EDITORIAL ESSAYS include guest editorials from some of the best thinkers and researchers in EP today;

ORIGINAL RESEARCH provides empirical evidence for various EP methods;

CLINICAL REPORTS describe the use of EP with challenging conditions and specific populations and provide guidance for empirical research;

INTERFACES WITH OTHER THERAPIES show how EP is typically used in conjunction with other methods, such as cognitive behavior therapy (CBT), mindfulness therapy, addiction counseling, sports psychology, medicine, energy medicine, meditation, and life coaching;

REVIEW ARTICLES are theoretical papers, literature reviews, reports of innovations, and analyses that explore issues from the professional condition of EP to the physiological mechanisms of action of EP;

BOOK REVIEWS cover new and classic EP-related titles;

ABSTRACTS published in other journals relevant to EP are reprinted.

EDITORIAL BOARD

EDITORIAL ESSAY

Getting Today's Medicine Today: The Challenge of Clinical Innovation

Dawson Church

The history of science is littered with examples of technology driving discovery. The Human Genome Project was driven by the availability of gene-sequencing machines. According to a report from the U.S. National Institutes of Health, in 2001, it cost an average of $95,263,072 to sequence the genome of a single human being. In 2014, it cost $4,008 (Wetterstrand, 2014). Figure 1 shows the reductions in costs. As the technology became available, it was utilized for the scientific enterprise, driving down costs.

Not all technologies have been quickly or widely accepted, and the rapid adoption of new techniques is the exception rather than the norm. The adoption of new therapies such as Energy Psychology has been slowed by the inertia of large organizations. For instance, Emotional Freedom Techniques (EFT) was presented to the Veterans Administration as a treatment for posttraumatic stress disorder (PTSD) soon after the first cohort of veterans began arriving back from deployment in Iraq (Church, Feinstein, Palmer-Hoffman, Stein, & Tranguch, 2014). In 2009, Senator Carl Levin, chair of the Senate Armed Services Committee, wrote a personal letter to then Secretary for Veterans Affairs Eric Shinseki. He enclosed preliminary data on EFT's efficacy for PTSD and urged investigation by the VA. Shinseki took no action on this request.

Frustration with the lack of progress at the VA, knowledge of the growing research base, and anecdotes by constituents who were veterans prompted members of Congress to write another long and detailed letter to Shinseki in 2010, requesting seven concrete actions by the VA. Copies were circulated among other agencies, such as the National Institutes of Health. Two sets of hearings before congressional committees presented the evidence that EFT could remediate PTSD in six treatment sessions. Again, all this activity produced no interest within the VA in exploring or implementing EFT. This inability to translate scientific discovery into practical patient care is called a "translational gap."

The U.S. Congress commissioned a report by the Institute of Medicine (IOM) to determine

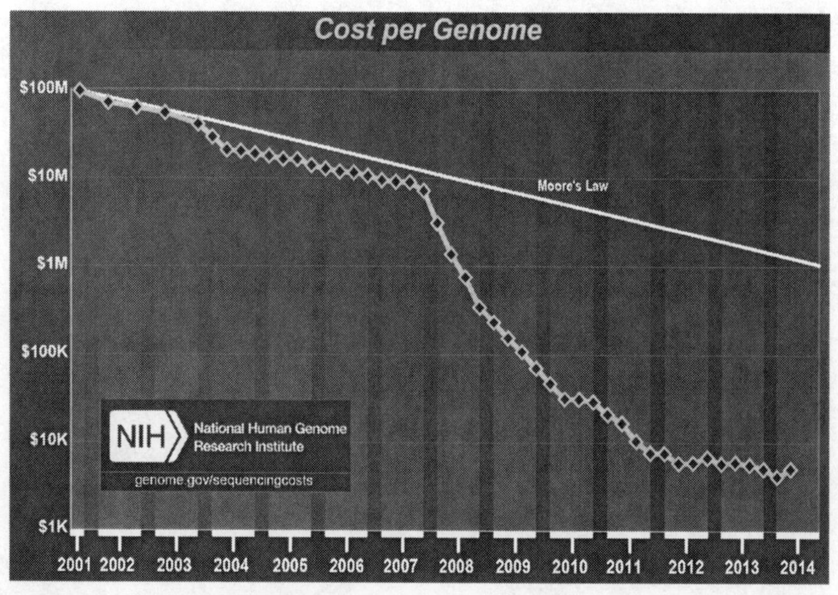

Figure 1. The cost of sequencing a human genome.

the extent of translational gaps. It found that it takes an average of 17 years for innovations to jump the translational gap (Committee on Quality of Health Care in America, IOM, 2001; Balas & Boren, 2000). Few innovations even make it that far: An analysis found that only 14% of new discoveries are successfully implemented in patient care; the other 86% are lost (Westfall, Mold, & Fagnan, 2007).

The IOM report characterized the translational gap as a "chasm." The practical consequences of this chasm are that most medical care that patients receive is 14% of what was available 17 years ago.

It's hard to imagine us, as a society, being content with this level of inefficiency in other parts of our lives. Imagine working on a 17-year-old personal computer, with 86% of its capacity disabled. While we'd be outraged at the detriment to our productivity and life enjoyment entailed by a reduction in our computing capacity, as a society we seem perfectly prepared to accept these limitations when it comes to our health care.

When I address this subject in professional circles, some listeners wonder if there's a conspiracy by the drug companies to suppress free and effective behavioral cures. Personally, I don't believe this (or most other conspiracy theories), because there are much simpler explanations. When I was talking to a military psychiatrist, Charles Engel, MD, about adopting EFT, he gave me a reality check. He told me that they can't even get the psychiatrist at the VA to coordinate care with the psychiatrist who has been treating that same patient while on active duty. Faced with fundamental obstacles like this, training in new therapies seems like a pipedream, no matter how effective those therapies may be.

This type of institutional inertia combines with dogmatic skepticism to produce most of the translational gap. That's why German physicist Max Planck remarked that science progresses one funeral at a time. Existing "experts" cling to their outdated worldviews, and not till a new generation has displaced them is there a more open intellectual climate in which new ideas can thrive. Highly effective new treatments sometimes overcome the inertia, however, though it might take awhile.

Seventeenth-century Dutch tradesman Anton van Leeuwenhoek was one of my heroes when I was a teenager. Leeuwenhoek perfected the art of grinding magnifying lenses, and began describing the curious microorganisms he saw through them. His curiosity was boundless, and he used his microscopes to examine organisms existing everywhere from ponds to human saliva.

He began reporting his findings to the newly formed Royal Society in England. At that time in history, the Royal Society was the most prestigious association in the world for the advancement of scientific enquiry. Leeuwenhoek's letters, translated into English, also contained painstaking drawings of the organisms he observed. While contemporary microscopes could magnify to only about 30x, Leeuwenhoek obsessively ground very fine lenses that could magnify an object by up to 200x. He began to see levels of detail in microscopic organisms that had never before been visible to the human eye. However, because these details had never before been observed, many members of the Royal Society greeted Leeuwenhoek's discoveries with hostile skepticism.

This kind of skepticism has impeded the progress of science for centuries. When Ignaz Semmelweiss in 1850s Vienna discovered that washing his hands between dissecting corpses in the morgue and examining patients in the wards reduced infections, he was disbelieved. He insisted on hospital workers washing their hands before treating patients. Infections in his ward dropped by 90%, while they remained at the same high levels in other wards. Nonetheless, Semmelweiss was vigorously opposed by his contemporaries, and eventually forced from his job. He died in an insane asylum, and his policies were immediately reversed by his successor. The history of science is littered with similar examples, from Lister to Galileo.

Dogmatic skepticism and anti-scientific superstition are alive and well today, impeding patient care as effectively as did Semmelweiss's contemporaries. You can read a contemporary example by looking up "EFT" on Wikipedia. Several years ago, a group of skeptics seized editorial control of most of the CAM (complementary and alternative medicine) pages on Wikipedia. Among the topics they control are homeopathy, energy psychology, and acupuncture.

The early articles were written mostly by experts in their fields. The skeptics deleted those articles, and wrote their own. They tag EFT and similar therapies as "pseudoscience," and whenever experts attempt to correct them, for instance by adding a description of a study newly published in a peer-reviewed journal, the skeptics suppress the amendment. To support their arguments, however, they selectively violate Wikipedia's own rules by citing skeptical websites and non-peer-reviewed (and non-credible) sources such as the *Skeptical Inquirer* magazine and Quackwatch.

A popular misconception is that anyone can edit a Wikipedia page; in reality, many entries are controlled by informal committees of editors, who can band together around a common philosophy, such as closed-minded hostility to CAM, or anti-scientific skepticism. The skeptics are organized as Wikiproject Skepticism, and they have vandalized hundreds of entries. In addition, certain pages have been locked to prevent open editing. The EFT page is one of them. These gatekeepers can then dictate what goes on a page, depriving the public using the encyclopedia from reading authoritative, balanced, and objective coverage of a topic, entries written by experienced and qualified experts. Another tactic of the Wikiproject Skepticism editors has been to delete or vandalize the biographies of respected scientists, authors, and researchers in the fields they attack.

Having demonstrated their worldview by tagging EFT as "pseudoscience" in the Wikipedia entry, how do they then deal with the inconvenient fact that there are dozens of clinical trials showing EFT's efficacy? Their solution is to simply not mention them in the article. Research doesn't support their prejudices, so they ignore it, even though clinical trials are routinely reported in entries for conventional therapies not targeted by the skeptics and in the entries for pharmacological drugs.

Wikipedia allows the reader to peer behind the entry to the history of additions and deletions to the article in the "Talk" pages, and the skeptical editors are perfectly clear, in these discussions, about their worldview. When new studies are published in peer-reviewed medical or psychology journals, the editors state that they should not be included in the Wikipedia article, as this might lend credibility to EFT, which in their eyes it does not have. One of the authors of the EFT entry debates "the best way to demonstrate to the reader that this is bullsh*t!" (http://en.wikipedia.org/wiki/Talk:Emotional_Freedom_Techniques/Archives/2011/May).

There is no mention in the Wikipedia article, or the behind-the-scenes discussions, of the standards for empirically validated therapies published by the Division 12 Task Force of the American Psychological Association, APA (Chambless & Hollon, 1998; Chambless et al., 1998). There is no reference to the evidence-based criteria embraced by the U.S. government's National Registry of Evidence-Based Programs and Practices (NREPP), or any description of the randomized controlled trials that have demonstrated EFT's efficacy for PTSD, depression, pain, anxiety, phobias, and other conditions.

Imagine a reputable encyclopedia, perhaps the *Encyclopedia Britannica,* writing an article by assembling an editorial team with complete ignorance of the topic, hostility to the field, scientific illiteracy, and no relevant academic qualifications. If the article's topic was the nature of the solar system, the team would contain not a single astronomer, physicist, or geologist. The only requirement would be that every contributor be a member of the Flat Earth Society. Absurd though it may seem, that's how most Wikipedia entries for CAM are created.

As comedian Tina Fey quipped, "When you're contemplating open-heart surgery, imagine your reaction to a guy who says, 'I don't have any of those fancy degrees from Harvard Medical School. I'm just an unlicensed plumber with a dream. Now hand me the scalpel.'"

Leeuwenhoek persisted despite the skepticism. Though he never wrote a book, he eventually exchanged hundreds of letters with members of the Royal Society. As the evidence mounted, the nonsensical superstitions of the skeptics were swept away, and Leeuwenhoek gained a secure place in scientific history.

In the same way, I expect the rapidly accumulating evidence for the efficacy of EFT and other evidence-based CAM interventions to overwhelm the efforts of the skeptics to prevent its dissemination. The system that perpetuates the translational chasm is still firmly in place, however, and until public demand for getting today's medicine today becomes an outcry, it is likely to remain entrenched.

References

Balas, E. A. & Boren, S. A. (2000). *Yearbook of medical informatics: Managing clinical knowledge for health care improvement.* Stuttgart, Germany: Schattauer Verlagsgesellschaft mbH.

Chambless, D., Baker, M. J., Baucom, D. H., Beutler, L. E., Calhoun, K. S., Crits-Christoph, P., … Woody, S. R. (1998). Update on empirically validated therapies, II. *Clinical Psychologist, 51*, 3–16.

Chambless, D. & Hollon, S. D. (1998). Defining empirically supported therapies. *Journal of Consulting and Clinical Psychology, 66*, 7–18.

Church, D., Feinstein, D., Palmer-Hoffman, J., Stein, P. K., & Tranguch, A. (2014). Empirically supported psychological treatments: The challenge of evaluating clinical innovations. *Journal of Nervous and Mental Disease, 202*(10), 699–709.

Committee on Quality of Health Care in America, Institute of Medicine. (2001). *Crossing the quality chasm: A new health system for the 21st century.* Washington, DC: National Academy Press.

Westfall, J. M., Mold, J., & Fagnan, L. (2007). Practice-based research: "Blue Highways" on the NIH roadmap. *JAMA, 297*(4), 403.

Wetterstrand, K. A. (2014). DNA sequencing costs: Data from the NHGRI Genome Sequencing Program (GSP). Retrieved from www.genome.gov/sequencingcosts

ORIGINAL RESEARCH

Effects of Emotional Freedom Techniques (EFT) on the Reduction of Chronic Pain in Adults: A Pilot Study

Nick Ortner, The Tapping Solution Foundation
Julie Palmer-Hoffman, National Institute for Integrative Healthcare
Morgan Ann Clond, Ben Gurion University Medical School

Abstract

This pilot study examined the effects of Emotional Freedom Techniques (EFT) on pain reduction in adults with chronic pain. A brief exposure therapy that combines cognitive and somatic elements, EFT has previously been found to be effective in the treatment of a number of psychological conditions, including depression, anxiety, phobia, and posttraumatic stress disorder. Research into EFT's effect on the treatment of physical pain and somatic complaints is less well established. In the present study, 50 adults with chronic pain participated in a 3-day workshop to learn how to use EFT. Pain was measured on the Pain Catastrophizing Scale (PCS) and the Multidimensional Pain Inventory (MPI) immediately before and after treatment and at 1-month and 6-month follow-ups. Significant reductions were found on each of the PCS item scores (rumination, magnification, and helplessness) and on the PCS total score (–43%, $p < .001$). On the MPI, significant improvements were observed in pain severity, interference, life control, affective distress, and dysfunctional composite. At 6-month follow-up, reductions were maintained on the PCS (–42%, $p < .001$) but only on the life control item for the MPI. Findings suggest that EFT helps immediately reduce pain severity while also improving participants' ability to live with their pain. Although reductions in pain severity were observed at 1-month follow-up but not maintained in the long-term, participants continued to report an improved sense of control and ability to cope with their chronic pain. The results of this pilot study are consistent with the literature and suggest directions for further research.

Keywords: Emotional Freedom Techniques, EFT, chronic pain, catastrophizing, group therapy

Nick Ortner is the *New York Times* best-selling author of *The Tapping Solution* and producer of the documentary film *The Tapping Solution*. **Julie Palmer-Hoffman**, MA, is a freelance writer, editor, and researcher, with a focus in the social sciences and health care improvement. **Morgan Ann Clond**, PhD, is a medical student at the Medical School for International Health, Ben Gurion University, and a biostatistician for the National Institute for Integrative Healthcare. **Correspondence:** 39 Beverly Drive, Brookfield, CT 06804. E-mail: nick@thetappingsolution.com. **Disclosures:** Author Nick Ortner receives income from EFT publications and training.

In 2011, the Institute of Medicine (IOM) estimated that there are approximately 100 million Americans living with chronic pain, a number that exceeds the combined totals affected by heart disease, cancer, and diabetes. In medical treatment and lost productivity, it is estimated that chronic pain costs the economy $635 billion a year and comprises fully 14% of Medicare expenditures. Pain, in the IOM's assessment, is a significant public health challenge. The mechanisms contributing to chronic pain are complex and poorly understood. Experiences of pain and the management of pain are often unique to an individual, and there are significant barriers to treatment and management in primary care (IOM, 2011). Citing findings that people with chronic pain are often frequent users of complementary and alternative medicine (CAM; IOM, 2011, p. 93)—an indication, perhaps, that conventional medical interventions have failed them—the IOM report recommends further research into the mechanisms responsible for the efficacy of CAM interventions (p. 261).

Grounded in the principles underlying Thought Field Therapy (Callahan, 2001) but further developed by Gary Craig (Craig, 2010; Craig & Fowlie, 1995), Emotional Freedom Techniques (EFT) has emerged as one of the most widely used interventions in the field of energy psychology (EP). EP is a collective of CAM modalities that combine well-established evidence-based methods, such as exposure and cognitive restructuring, for the treatment of psychological conditions with techniques from non-Western approaches to healing, such as the stimulation of acupuncture points, or acupoints (Feinstein, 2012). In EFT, participants pair a negative cognition (exposure) with a self-acceptance statement (cognitive restructuring) while stimulating acupoints by tapping on specific parts of the body, the combination of which "quickly and permanently reduces maladaptive fear responses to traumatic memories and related cues" (Feinstein, 2010, p. 385). By the standards of Division 12 of the American Psychological Association for "empirically supported treatments" (Chambless et al., 1996, 1998; Chambless & Hollon, 1998; Task Force on Promotion and Dissemination of Psychological Procedures, 1995), EFT has been found effective in the treatment of anxiety, depression, posttraumatic stress disorder (PTSD), and phobias (as summarized in Church, Feinstein, Palmer-Hoffman, Stein, & Tranguch, 2014). It has, moreover, been found effective in a seemingly disparate number of populations—college students preparing for a test (Jain & Rubino, 2012; Sezgin & Özçan, 2009), individuals with public speaking anxiety (Jones, Thornton, & Andrews, 2011), veterans (Church & Brooks, 2014, Church, 2014; Church et al., 2013), hospital patients with PTSD (Karatzias et al., 2011), and health care providers at risk for job burnout (Church & Brooks, 2010)—and in a variety of delivery formats (e.g., in office, telephone-delivered, group therapy, and online therapy: Brattberg, 2008; Hartung & Stein, 2012; Stapleton et al., 2013).

EFT has also been used to treat a number of somatic symptoms and pain conditions such as migraines, facial neuralgia, back pain, and fibromyalgia (Brattberg, 2008). Brattberg (2008), for example, compared an 8-week Internet-based EFT treatment group ($n = 26$) with a waitlist control group ($n = 36$) in a sample of women diagnosed with fibromyalgia and on sick leave for at least 3 months. Results showed that pain catastrophizing measures, including rumination, magnification, and helplessness—markers of participants' ability to cope with pain—were significantly improved in the treatment group ($p < .01$) as were measures of pain, anxiety, and depression ($p < .05$). Brattberg's study highlighted important considerations in the way chronic pain is conceptualized and measured in the biopsychosocial model: as a complex interplay of biological, psychological, behavioral, and social-cultural factors (Gatchel, Peng, Peters, Fuchs, & Turk, 2007). Brattberg (2008, p. 30) speculated that EFT's utility for chronic pain sufferers is that it targets and helps reduce the "distressing and disabling influences of pain by moving the patient to a more peaceful place of acceptance."

Church and Brooks (2010) measured psychological distress, emotional distress, and self-rated pain in a sample of 216 health care workers attending five professional conferences over a 1-year period. Attendees were assessed before and after a 1-day instructional workshop on self-application of EFT and 90 days after the workshop. Although data on the longevity of participants' pain were not collected (i.e., this study did not specifically measure chronic pain), immediate effects were observed on the reduction of self-assessed pain, in the form of a 68% drop in physical pain ($p < .001$). Severity of psychological symptoms, as measured on the SA-45, the short form of the Symptom Checklist–90 (Davison et al., 1997), was significantly improved following EFT treatment ($p < .001$), and the majority of these gains were maintained at follow-up. It should be noted that this study was uncontrolled, although results were replicated across multiple conferences and health care provider samples.

Bougea and colleagues (2013) conducted a randomized controlled trial (RCT) with a sample of patients being treated for tension-type headache (TTH) in an outpatient headache clinic in Athens, Greece. Patients who met International Headache Society guidelines for frequent TTH were randomly assigned either to an EFT treatment group ($n = 19$) or to a treatment-as-usual control group ($n = 16$). The study found that both headache frequency and intensity dropped by more than half for participants in the EFT group and that other physical symptoms improved ($p < .001$).

Finally, both Church (2014) and Church and Palmer-Hoffman (2014) reported findings related to pain in an RCT studying the effects of EFT on veterans with PTSD. Church (2014) found not only that veterans experienced significant drops ($p < .0001$) in physical pain after EFT compared with a waitlist control group, but also that these reductions remained significant at 3- and 6-month follow-ups. Church and Palmer-Hoffman (2014) retrospectively analyzed these data for reductions in somatoform symptoms of traumatic brain injury and found that symptoms were reduced by 41% ($p < .0021$). Again, data on chronic pain were not specifically gathered in either study, although it should be noted that, by definition, a PTSD diagnosis is not made unless criteria symptoms persist for more than a month (American Psychiatric Association, 2013) and the majority of participants were veterans from the Vietnam War era and were thus likely to have been living with their symptoms for years.

As previously summarized, evidence for the use of EFT in treating chronic pain is not as well established as it is for several psychological conditions. The current study thus sought to add to the accumulating evidence for its efficacy.

Method

Participants

In this study, 50 subjects were recruited to participate in an EFT tapping training session for pain reduction. Participants were recruited via advertisement to subscribers of the Tapping Solution's e-mail list or had been forwarded the information by a subscriber to this list. There was a cost to participate in the 3-day workshop, and the only criterion for inclusion was self-reported chronic pain, as defined by the participant. Chronic pain is typically defined as pain lasting longer than several months, with baselines ranging from a minimum of 3 to 6 months (IOM, 2011, p. 33). Participants were accepted into the study on a first-come, first-serve basis, until a total of 50 were signed up. Additional participants were present at the workshop, but only the first 50 people who expressed an interest in participating in the study were assessed on pain measures.

Measures

Participants' pain was assessed using the Pain Catastrophizing Scale (PCS; Osman et al., 2000; Sullivan, Bishop, & Pivik, 1995) and the Multidimensional Pain Inventory (MPI; Kerns, Turk, & Rudy, 1985). Both are well-validated, reliable, and widely used instruments, as evidenced by their translation and adaptation into various countries in Europe (e.g., Germany: Verra et al., 2012; Sweden: Jakobsson, 2009; Italy: Monticone et al., 2012; Norway: Fernandes, Storheim, Lochting, & Grotle, 2012; and France: Laliberté et al., 2008), Asia (Taiwan: Lai et al., 2009; Korea: Cho, Kim, & Lee, 2013), and South America (Brazil: Sehn et al., 2012).

The PCS, measuring participants' ability to cope with pain, consists of 13 statements that subjects are asked to rate on a scale of 1–5, corresponding to their agreement with the statement when they are experiencing pain. Ratings range from 0 (*not at all*) to 5 (*all the time*). Statements are evaluated as an overall score and also categorized into three areas: rumination, magnification, and helplessness.

The MPI is based on the biopsychosocial model of pain (McKillop & Nielson, 2011) and consists of 28 questions. Some of the questions are answered on a scale of 0 (*not at all* or *no change*) to 6 (*extremely well* or *extreme change*), and some questions are answered on a scale of 0 (*never*) to 3 (*often*). Questions are categorized into 11 categories: pain severity, interference, life control, affective distress, support, punishing responses, solicitous responses, distracting responses, general activity, dysfunctional composite, and interpersonally distressed composite.

The PCS and the MPI were administered to participants before and after treatment and at follow-ups of 1 and 6 months posttreatment.

Procedure

The author, a certified EFT practitioner, demonstrated the intervention to the participants as a group during the course of a workshop spread over three 8-hour days. The intervention was demonstrated with fidelity to *The EFT Manual* (Craig, 2010). Participants self-applied EFT in the course of the workshop, and certain participants volunteered as demonstration subjects receiving EFT sessions in front of the group. Trained volunteers were also available for individual tapping sessions if participants requested individual coaching in the technique.

Following *The EFT Manual* (Craig, 2010), participants were asked to first identify the site of the pain in their body. Participants created an affirmative and self-accepting statement that related to this pain—for example, "Even though I have this pain in my back, I deeply and completely accept myself." In EFT, this type of statement is referred to as the "setup statement." Participants repeated this setup statement three times to begin, then continued repeating a reminder phrase (e.g., "pain in my back") as they tapped five to seven times on each of 12 specific acupoints on the body, which correspond to the end points of the meridians identified in traditional

Chinese medicine. Before and after each round of tapping, participants self-assessed their pain on the Subjective Units of Distress (SUD) Scale (Wolpe, 1973), a Likert-type scale ranging from 0 (*no distress or pain*) to 10 (*highest distress/pain possible*). Rounds of tapping continued until participants had reduced their pain to 0 or near 0 on the SUD Scale.

Following the workshop, participants were encouraged to continue using EFT for pain management. Data were not collected on what percentage of participants continued to use EFT or with what frequency they did so. A workbook summarizing the techniques presented at the workshop was given to participants for their reference. Participants were also given the opportunity to arrange three phone calls with the author for additional tapping sessions, which would then be audio-recorded and made available to the participant. Few participants utilized this option, and data were not collected about their usage. Finally, the author also provided participants with audio recordings of two approximately 7-minute-long meditative tapping sessions for their individual use.

Statistical Analysis

Matched *t* tests were used to compare scores on the PCS and MPI before and after training, at 30-day follow-up, and at 6-month follow-up. A Bonferroni-corrected alpha level of 0.0036 was used to adjust for multiple testing. Cronbach's alpha was calculated as a measure of internal consistency. All statistical tests were run using SPSS Version 17.

Results

Participant Characteristics

Demographic data for 50 participants are summarized in Table 1. Subjects had a mean age of 57, with a range of 35 to 72 years. Most of the subjects were women (86%). The majority were employed and had completed undergraduate college studies. A majority of the participants reported that they exercised regularly. Some subjects reported sleep disturbances due to pain, but the average number of reported hours of sleep per night was 6.8 hours. Participants were asked to rate their pain on a scale of 0–10. The average pain scale rating was 8, indicating severe pain.

Changes in Test Scores

Statistically significant score reductions were found in each of the PCS item scores (rumination, magnification, and helplessness) and the PCS total score ($p < .001$). These results are summarized in Table 2. The subscore for helplessness had the largest reduction. Only six subjects did not have a reduction in total PCS score. The PCS total score had a Cronbach's alpha of 0.76, indicating a high level of internal consistency for this sample.

Table 1: *Participant Characteristics (*N *= 50)*

Characteristics	$M \pm SD$ (Range)	*n* (%)
Age	57 (35–72)	
Gender		43 (86%)
Employment status		
Employed or self-employed		29 (58%)
Unemployed or disabled		5 (10%)
Not in workforce or retired		14 (30%)
Years of education	17 ± 3.6	
Any exercise		43 (86%)
Average sleep hours	6.8 ± 1.3	
Pain rating (1–10)	8 ± 1.6	

For the MPI, significant improvements were noted in pain severity, interference, life control, affective distress, and dysfunctional composite (see Table 3). Scores for support, punishing responses, solicitous responses, distracting responses, general activity, and interpersonally distressed composite were unchanged.

Follow-up Changes

Nine subjects did not complete the PCS at the 1-month follow-up, leaving 41 subjects. Between 1 month and 6 months, an additional 7 subjects were lost to follow-up, leaving 34 subjects for analysis.

Follow-up evaluations determined that participants maintained significant improvements in PCS scores at 1-month and 6-month follow-ups (see Table 4), with the exception of magnification at 1-month follow-up. The reduction in magnification score at 1-month follow-up was lower on average than the baseline but not statistically different.

When posttest scores were compared with follow-up at 1 month or 6 months, no significant changes were noted, indicating that score changes were maintained over the duration of the follow-up period.

Table 2: *Pain Catastrophizing Scale (PCS) Pretest versus Posttest Scores (*N *= 50)*

Score	Pretest ($M \pm SD$)	Posttest ($M \pm SD$)	Change in $M \pm SEM$	t	p
Rumination	9.8 ± 4.2	6.0 ± 4.6	3.8 ± 0.6	6.5	<.001*
Magnification	5.3 ± 2.8	3.5 ± 2.5	1.7 ± 3.1	4.0	<.001*
Helplessness	11.7 ± 6.5	6.0 ± 5.0	5.7 ± 0.8	7.4	<.001*
Total	26.5 ± 11.6	15.5 ± 10.9	11.0 ± 10.6	7.3	<.001*

*Significant after Bonferroni correction.

At 1-month follow-up, 10 subjects did not complete the MPI, leaving 40 subjects. Between 1 month and 6 months, an additional six subjects were lost to follow-up, leaving 34 subjects for analysis.

As shown in Table 5, a statistically significant improvement in life control was noted at 6-month follow-up but not 1-month follow-up. The change in life control between the 1-month follow-up and the 6-month follow-up was significant. Interference and pain severity decreased significantly after treatment and remained significantly reduced at 1 month. However, at 6 months, the difference was no longer significant after Bonferroni correction. Affective distress was reduced after treatment but was not found to be significantly reduced at 1-month or 6-month follow-ups.

Discussion

The present study found improvements on measures of pain severity, pain catastrophizing, and the impact of pain on an individual's life and general activity following a 3-day workshop teaching participants to use self-applied EFT. Reductions in pain catastrophizing, a maladaptive response that may contribute to the chronicity of pain (Sehn et al., 2012) and has been found to be a key predictor of disability (Fernandes et al., 2012), were maintained at both 1- and 6-month follow-ups, as was improved life control on the MPI at the 6-month follow-up, suggesting that following EFT, participants were better able to cope with their chronic pain. This is noteworthy given that

Table 3: *Multidimensional Pain Inventory (MPI) Pretest versus Posttest Scores (*N *= 50)*

Score	Pretest ($M \pm SD$)	Posttest ($M \pm SD$)	Change in $M \pm SEM$	t	p
Pain Severity	53.1 ± 18.0	41.8 ± 13.8	11.3 ± 1.8	6.3	<.001*
Interference	55.6 ± 13.6	48.9 ± 14.3	6.8 ± 1.1	6.1	<.001*
Life Control	55.0 ± 14.1	63.2 ± 14.3	–8.1 ± 2.0	–4.1	<.001*
Affective Distress	49.7 ± 13.0	40.6 ± 14.7	9.1 ± 1.9	4.7	<.001*
Support	54.2 ± 17.9	53.8 ± 21.4	0.42 ± 1.4	0.3	.77
Punishing Responses	28.7 ± 29.2	27.6 ± 24.8	1.1 ± 2.2	0.5	.60
Solicitous Responses	48.0 ± 18.6	48.4 ± 18.9	–0.4 ± 1.2	–0.4	.72
Distracting Responses	49.1 ± 22.5	49.3 ± 23.5	–0.14 ± 2.27	–0.1	.95
General Activity	56.8 ± 5.9	56.2 ± 6.7	0.56 ± 0.63	0.9	.39
Dysfunctional Composite	48.4 ± 10.2	41.4 ± 9.2	7.03 ± 1.0	6.8	<.001*
Interpersonally Distressed Composite	44.6 ± 12.0	45.5 ± 11.5	–0.9 ± 0.7	–1.2	.23

*Significant after Bonferroni correction.

Table 4: *PCS with Follow-up*

Score	Pretest ($M \pm SD$)	Posttest ($M \pm SD$)	1-month follow-up ($M \pm SD$)	6-month follow-up ($M \pm SD$)	$p^{§}$
Rumination	9.8 ± 4.2	6.0 ± 4.6	6.7 ± 4.7	5.9 ± 3.9	<.001*
Magnification	5.3 ± 2.8	3.5 ± 2.5	4.0 ± 2.8	3.4 ± 2.5	<.001*
Helplessness	11.7 ± 6.5	6.0 ± 5.0	6.7 ± 5.1	6.5 ± 5.0	<.001*
Total	26.5 ± 11.6	15.5 ± 10.9	17.4 ± 11.3	15.6 ± 10.0	<.001*

*Significant after Bonferroni correction.
§*p* values are given for pretest versus 6-month follow-up.

reductions in pain severity, observed immediately and 1 month after the intervention, were not maintained over the long-term.

These results should be interpreted with caution. This study used a convenience sample composed of participants enrolled in a paid workshop to learn EFT for pain management and therefore could be assumed to be highly motivated participants. The same degree of motivation is unlikely to be found in the larger population pain patients. Attrition (approximately 20% at 1 month and 32% at 6 months) may have skewed the results. This study lacked a comparison or control group, did not collect data on the length or source of the chronic pain participants experienced, and did not track participants' subsequent use of EFT following the workshop. Future controlled studies should be designed to address these limitations. Nonetheless, the symptom improvements found in the current study closely track those reported in RCTs conducted by Brattberg (2008), Church (2014), and Bougea et al., (2013) in participants experiencing chronic pain associated with fibromyalgia and tension-type headache, and with veterans.

If these results can be replicated in an RCT for individuals suffering from chronic pain and it can furthermore be demonstrated that participants maintain their gains over time (limitations that

Table 5: *MPI with Follow-up*

Score	Pretest ($M \pm SD$)	Posttest ($M \pm SD$)	1-month follow-up ($M \pm SD$)	6-month follow-up ($M \pm SD$)	$p^{§}$
Pain Severity	53.1 ± 18.0	41.8 ± 13.8	40.9 ± 18.4	50.8 ± 17.5	.18
Interference	55.6 ± 13.6	48.9 ± 14.3	43.6 ± 17.4	52.8 ± 12.3	.01
Life Control	55.0 ± 14.1	63.2 ± 14.3	56.7 ± 20.3	71.1 ± 16.9	<.001*
Affective Distress	49.7 ± 13.0	40.6 ± 14.7	44.8 ± 15.9	46.9 ± 12.7	.03
Support	54.2 ± 17.9	53.8 ± 21.4	54.8 ± 16.5	61.5 ± 14.0	.07
Punishing Responses	28.7 ± 29.2	27.6 ± 24.8	25.8 ± 27.2	31.0 ± 29.3	.80
Solicitous Responses	48.0 ± 18.6	48.4 ± 18.9	48.6 ± 16.7	52.7 ± 15.6	.85
Distracting Responses	49.1 ± 22.5	49.3 ± 23.5	46.0 ± 24.4	52.9 ± 19.3	.63
General Activity	56.8 ± 5.9	56.2 ± 6.7	57.1 ± 5.5	56.1 ± 6.0	.77
Dysfunctional Composite	48.4 ± 10.2	41.4 ± 9.2	46.0 ± 24.4	52.9 ± 19.3	.32
Interpersonally Distressed Composite	44.6 ± 12.0	45.5 ± 11.5	46.2 ± 9.5	41.6 ± 9.6	.75

*Significant after Bonferroni correction.
§*p* values are given for pretest versus 6-month follow-up.

prevent the generalization of results from Bougea et al., [2013] and Brattberg, [2008]), the implications would be considerable. Among its recommendations, the IOM (2011) highlights promotion of self-management of pain and the reduction of barriers to pain care as strategies to address the "public health challenge" of chronic pain. Whereas chronic pain currently costs the U.S. economy an estimated $638 billion a year, EFT is low-cost; can be delivered in group format (Church & Brooks, 2010, 2014), via the Internet (Brattberg, 2008), and over the phone (Hartung & Stein, 2012); and can also be self-administered (Brattberg, 2008). Particularly when there are barriers to accessing primary-care resources for pain treatment and management, EFT presents a relatively low-cost and straightforward alternative to conventional medical interventions for chronic pain, offering individuals improved feelings of control and the ability to cope with their pain. Additional controlled studies in populations with chronic pain should explore this potential.

References

American Psychiatric Association. (2013). *Diagnostic and statistical manual of mental disorders* (5th ed.). Washington, DC: Author.

Bougea, A. M., Spandideas, N., Alexopoulos, E. C., Thomaides, T., Chrousos, G. P., & Darviri, C. (2013). Effect of the Emotional Freedom Technique on perceived stress, quality of life, and cortisol salivary levels in tension-type headache sufferers: A randomized controlled trial. *Explore: The Journal of Science and Healing, 9*, 91–99. doi:10.1016/j.explore.2012.12.005

Brattberg, G. (2008). Self-administered EFT (Emotional Freedom Techniques) in individuals with fibromyalgia: A randomized trial. *Integrative Medicine*, *7*(4), 30–35.

Callahan, R. (2001). Raising and lowering of heart rate variability: Some clinical findings of Thought Field Therapy. *Journal of Clinical Psychology, 57*, 1175–1186.

Chambless, D., Baker, M. J., Baucom, D. H., Beutler, L. E., Calhoun, K. S., Crits-Christoph, P., . . . Woody, S. R. (1998). Update on empirically validated therapies: II. *Clinical Psychologist, 51*, 3–16.

Chambless, D. & Hollon, S. D. (1998). Defining empirically supported therapies. *Journal of Consulting and Clinical Psychology, 66*, 7–18.

Chambless, D. L., Sanderson, W. C., Shoham, V., Bennett Johnson, S., Pope, K. S., Crits-Christoph, P., . . . McCurry, S. (1996). An update on empirically validated therapies. *Clinical Psychologist, 49*, 5–18.

Cho, S., Kim, H. Y., & Lee, J. H. (2013). Validation of the Korean version of the Pain Catastrophizing Scale in patients with chronic non-cancer pain. *Quality of Life Research, 22*, 1767–1772.

Church, D. (2014). Pain, depression, and anxiety after PTSD remediation in veterans. *Explore: The Journal of Science and Healing* (in press).

Church, D. & Brooks, A. J. (2010). The effect of brief Emotional Freedom Techniques self-intervention on anxiety, depression, pain, and cravings in health care workers. *Integrative Medicine, 9*(5), 40–43.

Church, D. & Brooks, A. J. (2014). CAM and energy psychology techniques remediate PTSD symptoms in veterans and spouses. *Explore: The Journal of Science and Healing, 10*, 24–33.

Church, D., Feinstein, D., Palmer-Hoffman, J., Stein, P. K., & Tranguch, A. (2014). Empirically supported psychological treatments: The challenge of evaluating clinical innovations. *Journal of Nervous and Mental Disease* (in press).

Church, D., Hawk, C., Brooks, A., Toukolehto, O., Wren, M., Dinter, I., & Stein, P. (2013). Psychological trauma symptom improvement in veterans using EFT (Emotional Freedom Techniques): A randomized controlled trial. *Journal of Nervous and Mental Disease, 201*, 153–160.

Church, D. & Palmer-Hoffman. J. (2014). TBI symptoms improve after PTSD remediation with Emotional Freedom Techniques. *Traumatology* (in press).

Craig, G. (2010). *The EFT manual.* Santa Rosa, CA: Energy Psychology Press.

Craig, G. & Fowlie, A. (1995). *Emotional Freedom Techniques: The manual.* Sea Ranch, CA: Gary Craig.

Davison, M. L., Bershadsky, B., Bieber, J., Silversmith, D., Maruish, M. K., & Kane, R. L. (1997). Development of a brief, multidimensional, self-report instrument for treatment outcomes assessment in psychiatric settings: Preliminary findings. *Assessment, 4*, 259–275.

Feinstein, D. (2010). Rapid treatment of PTSD: Why psychological exposure with acupoint tapping may be effective. *Psychotherapy Theory, Research, Practice, Training, 47*, 385–402. doi:10.1037/a0021171

Feinstein, D. (2012). Acupoint stimulation in treating psychological disorders: Evidence of efficacy. *Review of General Psychology, 16*, 364–380. doi:10.1037/a0028602

Fernandes, L., Storheim, K., Lochting, I., & Grotle, M. (2012). Cross-cultural adaptation and validation of the Norwegian Pain Catastrophizing Scale in patients with low back pain. *BMC Musculoskeletal Disorders, 13*, 111.

Gatchel, R. J., Peng, Y. B., Peters, M. L., Fuchs, P. N., & Turk, D. C. (2007). The biopsychosocial approach to chronic pain: Scientific advances and future directions. *Psychological Bulletin, 133*, 581–624.

Hartung, J. & Stein, P. K. (2012). Telephone delivery of EFT (Emotional Freedom Techniques) remediates PTSD symptoms in veterans: A randomized controlled trial. *Energy Psychology: Theory, Research, and Treatment, 4*(1), 33–42. doi:10.9769.EPJ.2012.4.1.JH

Institute of Medicine (IOM). (2011). *Relieving pain in America: A blueprint for transforming prevention, care, education, and research.* Washington, DC: National Academies Press.

Jain, S. & Rubino, A. (2012) The effectiveness of Emotional Freedom Techniques (EFT) for optimal test performance: A randomized controlled trial. *Energy Psychology: Theory, Research, and Treatment, 4*, 13–24. doi:10.9769.EPJ.2012.4.2.SJ

Jakobsson, U. (2009). Psychometric testing of the brief screening version of Multidimensional Pain Inventory (Swedish version). *Scandinavian Journal of Caring Sciences, 23*, 171–179.

Jones, S., Thornton, J., & Andrews, H. (2011). Efficacy of EFT in reducing public speaking anxiety: A randomized controlled trial. *Energy Psychology: Theory, Research, and Treatment, 3*(1), 19–32. doi:10.9769.EPJ.2011.3.1.SJ

Karatzias, T., Power, K., Brown, K., McGoldrick, T., Begum, M., Young, J., . . . Adams, S. (2011). A controlled comparison of the effectiveness and efficiency of two psychological therapies for posttraumatic stress disorder: Eye movement desensitization and reprocessing vs. Emotional Freedom Techniques. *Journal of Nervous and Mental Disease, 199*, 372–378. doi:10.1097/NMD.0b013e31821cd262.

Kerns, R. D., Turk, D. C., & Rudy, T. E. (1985). The West Haven–Yale Multidimensional Pain Inventory (WHYMPI). *Pain, 23*, 345–356.

Lai, Y. H., Guo, S. L., Keefe, F. J., Tsai, L. Y., Shun, S. C., Liao, Y. C., . . . Lee, Y. H. (2009). Multidimensional Pain Inventory–Screening Chinese version (MPI-sC): Psychometric testing in terminal cancer patients in Taiwan. *Supportive Care in Cancer, 17*, 1445–1453.

Laliberté, S., Lamoureux, J., Sullivan, M. J., Miller, J. M., Charron, J., & Bouthilier, D. (2008). French translation of the Multidimensional Pain Inventory: L'inventaire multidimensionnel de la douleur. *Pain Research and Management, 13*, 497–505.

McKillop, J. M. & Nielson, W. R. (2011). Improving the usefulness of the Multidimensional Pain Inventory. *Pain Research and Management, 16*, 239–244.

Monticone, M., Baiardi, P., Ferrari, S., Foti, C., Mugnai, R., Pillastrini, P., . . . Vanti, C. (2012). Development of the Italian version of the Pain Catastrophizing Scale (PCS-I): Cross-cultural adaptation, factor analysis, reliability, validity and sensitivity to change. *Quality of Life Research, 21*, 1045–1050.

Osman, A., Barrios, F. X., Gutierrez, P. M., Kopper, B. A., Merrifield, T., & Grittman, L. (2000). The Pain Catastrophizing Scale: Further psychometric evaluation with adult samples. *Journal of Behavioral Medicine, 23*, 351–365.

Sehn, F., Chachamovich, E., Vidor, L. P., Dall-Agnol, L., de Souza, I. C., Torres, I. L., . . . Caumo, W. (2012). Cross-cultural adaptation and validation of the Brazilian Portuguese version of the Pain Catastrophizing Scale. *Pain Medicine, 13*, 1425–1435.

Sezgin, N. & Özcan, B. (2009). The effect of progressive muscular relaxation and Emotional Freedom Techniques on test anxiety in high school students: A randomized controlled trial. *Energy Psychology: Theory, Research, and Treatment, 1*, 23–30. doi:10.9769.EPJ.2009.1.1.NS.

Stapleton, P., Church, D., Sheldon, T., Porter, B., & Carlopio, C. (2013). Depression symptoms improve after successful weight loss with Emotional Freedom Techniques. *ISRN Psychiatry, 2013*, 573532. doi:10.1155/2013/573532.

Sullivan, M. J., Bishop, S. R., & Pivik, J. (1995). The Pain Catastrophizing Scale: Development and validation. *Psychological Assessment, 7*, 524–532.

Task Force on Promotion and Dissemination of Psychological Procedures. (1995). Training in and dissemination of empirically validated psychological treatments: Report and recommendations. *Clinical Psychologist, 48*, 3–23.

Verra, M. L., Angst, F., Staal, J. B., Brioschi, R., Lehmann, S., Aeschilmann, A., & de Bie, R. A. (2012). Reliability of the Multidimensional Pain Inventory and stability of the MPI classification system in chronic back pain. *BMC Musculoskeletal Disorders, 24*, 155. doi:10.1186/1471-2474-13-155

Wolpe, J. (1973). *The practice of behavior therapy*. New York, NY: Pergamon Press.

Simple versus Complex Trauma: A Clinician's Guide to Indications, Treatment Plans, and Therapeutic Methods

Yves Wauthier-Freymann, Training Institute for Psychotherapy, Brussels, Belgium

Abstract

This clinical report is intended to guide practitioners in the identification and treatment of simple and complex trauma. It addresses the questions: How can the clinician distinguish between a simple trauma and a complex trauma? How can attachment disorders be managed, and what impact do they have on the processing of traumatic memories? What type of treatment plan is indicated once the nature of the trauma has been identified? When these questions are answered, treatment can proceed efficiently. A structured approach for assessing trauma is presented, beginning with the defining characteristics of simple and complex trauma. A three-stage treatment plan is presented for each of the two types of trauma. This structure enables the identification of interventions that are safe and appropriate for the client, operating within a therapeutic range that avoids the extremes of abreaction (overwhelming emotional release) and dissociation from emotional and physical sensation. Intervention includes elements drawn from energy psychology, heart coherence, Internal Family Systems, and Compassion Focused Therapy (CFT). This approach remediates successfully most psychological trauma.

Keywords: simple trauma, complex trauma, energy psychology, treatment plan, client safety

Yves Wauthier, president of the Training Institute for Psychotherapy Therapeutia, Belgium representative to ACEP, and president of Francophone Association for Clinical Energy Psychology (APEC), is a psychotherapist specializing in brief therapy and posttraumatic stress management. **Correspondence:** Avenue de Nivelles 39 à 1300 Limal, Brabant wallon, Belgique. Tel: 32 (0) 486 800 928; e-mail: info@yves-wauthier.com.
Disclosure: The author declares no conflicts of interest.

One of the challenges that therapists face in mapping out a treatment plan for a new client is identification of the trauma at the heart of the behavior or problem for which the client is seeking treatment. Differentiating between a simple and a complex trauma, which is not always easy, is crucial in this process because it can determine the effectiveness of treatment.

Clients often present with a request that seemingly has nothing to do with the trauma: They might want to stop smoking, to weaken an addiction, to address an obsessive behavior, or to remediate an underlying, nagging anxiety, for example. One of the advantages of a more clinical approach, then, is that it recognizes the actual scope of the client's trauma, apart from the client's self-identified symptoms. With that recognition, therapists can redefine the problematic behavior by helping clients identify the connection between earlier traumas and presenting symptoms, thereby helping restore their autonomy and regain control over and contact with their internal selves.

In this article, I offer ways of distinguishing between simple and complex traumas and present steps for creating treatment plans that are tailored to each type.

Simple Trauma (Type I)

Definition

A trauma comprises a physical or psychological wound inflicted on a person as well as the local or general consequences of that wound.

A simple trauma can be seen as the emotional imprint, or the trace, of a traumatic event within an individual, and includes the physical sensations and negative cognitions associated with the event. In general, a simple trauma stems from a single event, not one repeated over time. Though it may seem easy to identify a simple trauma, the trauma is sometimes hidden by the resilience of the client. This resilience is the skill to adapt quickly to every new situation that could cause difficulties; it is the survival instinct.

Treatment Plan

The treatment plan for a simple trauma is relatively straightforward. Ideally, the therapist works on the oldest event related to the problem. A technique called a *floatback* is used to reactivate clients' access to their oldest memories connected with whatever is triggering them today. It allows the client's subconscious to return effortlessly to that core memory or event. Here is the procedure. The technique is done as follows. When the client is clearly in full contact with the triggered emotions and the cognition (the belief) has been clarified, the therapist then asks the client to close her eyes and quickly asks what age she remembers herself as being on the first occasion she experienced this emotion. For example, I ask the client: What is the worse situation? What are your feelings, emotions? Here and now where do you feel them in your body? What are the sensations in your body? I wait about 10 seconds, then ask: At what age do you see yourself having felt that?

The purpose here is to use the memory of the body rather than the mind. When the client's floatback is guided properly, an image, feelings, or particular thought will instantly emerge. This often enables the client to identify a core scene, from which the therapist can start to treat past events.

Once the target event from the past has been desensitized, we can move back to the present and desensitize the triggers there as well. As a last step, we check a future projection by asking the client to envision herself in the situation from the past and then imagine herself reexperiencing the same type of event. If the treatment has been effective, there will be no doubt, no negative emotion, no limiting thoughts, and no unpleasant feelings related to the situations addressed.

Summary of Treatment Plan

1. Past (floatback): Work on the past by focusing on the most emotionally reactive event.
2. Next, focus on the present.
3. Finally, ask the client to visualize him or herself in the future, faced with a similar problem.

Complex Trauma (Type II)

Definition

Complex trauma stems from an accumulation of traumatic events endured or repeated over time. These events may be of the same nature or different. They may be concentrated in time or, on the contrary, spread out over many years.

The following is a summary of common categories of complex trauma and the symptoms that identify them (Mémoire traumatique et victimologie, n.d.).

Acute stress is characterized by the following symptoms:

- Distress
- Brief psychotic episodes
- Occurring up to 1 month after the traumatic event.

Posttraumatic stress (lasting more than 1 month), *chronic stress* (lasting more than 6 months), and *delayed stress* share the following symptoms:

- Reexperiencing. This can include recurring thoughts on the violence endured; dwelling on negative thoughts; experiencing intrusive memories of all or part of the event (e.g., feelings, pain, noise, or words); having flashbacks, illusions, recurring dreams, or intense nightmares that are perceived with a high level of anxiety and distress; or reacting suddenly as though the event were going to happen again. Childbirth can trigger reexperiencing.
- Avoidance. Individuals may avoid all situations related to the trauma or those situations that may remind them of it, or they may avoid thinking of the trauma or putting themselves in any potentially painful or stressful situation. They may develop an imaginary world, experience a dulling of emotions or a loss of positive anticipation of the future, or withdraw from interpersonal relationships.
- Hyperreactivity. Characterized by hypervigilance, a constant state of alertness and control, the ability to be easily startled, insomnia, nocturnal awakening, hypersensitivity, irritability, explosive anger, and poor concentration and focus.
- Dissociation. Often strong, it includes a state of altered awareness; poor memory, concentration, and focus; feelings of strangeness;

the impression of being a witness of one's own life; depersonalization; and even conjuring an imaginary companion.

Complex posttraumatic stress disorder refers to the consequences in victims of interpersonal violence that occurred repeatedly over a long period. It is defined by several criteria, some of which are also part of the definition of borderline personality:

- Altered ability to regulate emotions, with pronounced impulsiveness and self-destructive behaviors
- Disturbance of awareness and focus, which can lead to episodes of dissociation
- Altered perception of oneself, with constant feelings of shame or guilt and a feeling of emptiness
- Altered perception of the attacker, who may be idealized
- Disturbed interpersonal relations, with an inability to trust or to have intimate relations with others
- Symptoms of somatization
- Cognitive dissonance with a loss of hope.

Some people may also be more sensitive when they suffer from attachment disorder, which stems from a childhood in which emotional attachment failed to give the child a sense of security or reassurance, resulting in either anxious attachment or detachment.

Treatment Plan

These different possibilities in a client's psychological profile make it more complicated to determine a treatment plan and the order in which to work in therapy. The order is important to ensure that the therapist works in the most integrative (i.e., respectful and fitting with the client's overall life values and direction) and safest way possible for the client.

In contrast to simple traumas, complex traumas are not to be treated starting with the past. A properly structured treatment plan will avoid overwhelming the client, as generally happens when the targeting or assessment of the problem is inaccurate. Likewise, it is important to distinguish between the treatment plan, which covers the subjects, events, and relationships that have to be treated in a series of therapy sessions, and the plan for each individual session, which prescribes how a therapist will approach the focal event or topic to work on during a single session.

It is possible and may be necessary to revise the treatment plan as a result of what emerges during treatment sessions. Sometimes certain material appears for the first time during a session, either because the relationship—the therapeutic alliance—improves or because certain layers that prevented access to information have been resolved. When these barriers break down or other parts of the client's psyche appear during the session (parts that represent the different emotions that coexist with the trauma and exist to protect the client from being overwhelmed by the traumatic material), the treatment plan must be reassessed and possibly revised.

One of the key elements of the treatment is to keep the client, as much as possible, within a comfortable "window" by seeking to avoid *abreactions* (an overwhelming and painful emotional release) as well as its opposite, *dissociation* (the blocking out of all emotional or physical feeling).

Summary of Treatment Plan

1. Assess the strength of Self and availability of resources.
2. Identify triggers in the present.
3. Work on past events.

Treatment Plan in Practice: Detailed Protocol for Complex Trauma

Treatment for complex trauma begins by assessing the client's ability to create and maintain resources. The therapist may also begin by creating a space of security or serenity. Resources, in this context, are events, situations, thoughts, and people that have been positive forces in the client's life. It is best to choose resources that are related to the negative cognition that is the focus of treatment. The therapist should first seek to identify the negative belief, take its positive opposite (positive cognition), and next identify an event, situation, symbol, or person that illustrates this positive cognition in the client's life.

Below I describe nine steps based on the work of Korn and Leeds (2002) in order to illustrate, with sample treatment dialogue, how therapists can institute this approach in practice. At each stage, therapists can select the questions or instructions that correspond best to their respective clients.

1. Identify the Resources Needed for a Current Problem

Say to the client: *Think about a particularly challenging situation in your current life. You might think about therapy and the challenge of facing your trauma. Perhaps you're facing a challenging situation with a particular person in your life. When you think about this situation, what qualities, resources, or strengths are you missing? What do you need? What would you like to believe about yourself in this situation? How would you like to feel? What would you like to be able to do?*

Sample answers:

I'd like to feel stronger.
I'd like to feel more attached.
I'd like to feel more grounded.
I'd like to have more self-confidence.
I'd like to feel braver.
I'd like to feel more decisive.
I'd like to feel more flexible.
I want to increase my trust in the healing process.
I want to congratulate myself.
I want to be able to manage my emotions.
I want to be able to set my limits better.
I want to feel loved.
I want to be able to state my needs.

2. Identify the Types of Available Resources

2a. Identify successful experiences and associated images

Think of a time when you felt _______ (e.g., strong, safe, confident, soothed, able to tolerate your feelings). *Think of a time when you were able to behave with more* _______ (e.g., courage, self-trust, flexibility). *What experiences capture that desired quality or feeling?*

Are there parts of yourself that you rely on (e.g., your wise self, professional self, warrior self)? *Can you see an image of yourself in the future possessing the qualities or resources that you desire?*

2b. Identify relational resources (models and reference figures)

Think of people in your life, now or in the past, who possess or embody this quality. Think of who you would want in your corner, cheering you on, coaching you, helping you to feel _______ (e.g., stronger, supported, more confident). *Think about friends, relatives, teachers, caregivers, therapists. Think of any people out there in the world who possess or embody this quality, who serve or could serve as a role model for you* (e.g., TV stars, public figures, or characters in books, movies, or cartoons). *Think about your mentors, people who have made a difference in your life. Do you have a spiritual guide, someone or something that gives you hope or strength along the way? Are there any animals or pets that you associate with these positive feelings or qualities?*

2c. Identify metaphors and symbolic resources

Think of any other images, symbols, or metaphors that would help you feel ________ (e.g., soothed, loved, connected, protected, contained, peaceful). *Think of any positive images or symbols that have come up in your artwork, dreams or daydreams, or guided imagery exercises* (e.g., a strong yet flexible tree).

3. Develop Resources

Work on one resource at a time.

When you think about that ________ (e.g., experience, person, symbol), *what do you see? What do you hear? What do you smell? What emotions do you notice as you focus on this image or memory? What sensations do you experience in your body?*

Note the client's exact words so as to be able to use them throughout the treatment process.

4. Check the Resource

When you focus on _________ (repeat description of image) *and notice the* _________ (repeat description of feelings, sensations, smells, sounds, etc.), *how do you feel?*

Check that the resource selected can help the client deal with the problematic (target) situation, by asking:

When you focus on (the problematic situation), *how true or supportive do* (repeat the description of the image and feelings) *sound, on a scale of 0 to 10, where 0 is completely false and 10 is completely true or useful?*

5. Feel the Resource

Take the time to pause on this image __________ (repeat the description of the image) *and observe* ________________ (repeat the description of the sounds, smells, sensations and feelings, etc.).

Repeat the words that the client has used for the image, sounds, sensations, and feelings and vary the order of the sentences. Check whether the client is able to maintain this resource without there being negative associations, interferences, or emotions. Do not carry on with this resource if the client reports negative associations or emotions. In that case, start over again, with a different resource.

6. Install the Resource

While you remain focused on ____________ (repeat the words the client used to describe the image and the associated emotions and sensations), *take the TAT pose* (i.e., Tapas Acupressure Technique), *or tap.*

Clients should hold the pose or tap for only about 10 seconds. This should be repeated several times. After each time, ask the client: *What are you feeling or noticing now?*

Do not carry on with the TAT pose or tapping if the client reports negative associations or emotions. The negative material must be compartmentalized in an imaginary way, for example, in a safe or container, before carrying on. Otherwise the process must be started over again with another resource.

7. Strengthen the Resource by Means of Associations or Verbal or Sensory Points of Reference

The client should hold the TAT pose or tap briefly after each answer to the following, as long as the effect remains positive:

Imagine going a step further in connecting with this resource. As you remember that experience (e.g., for mastery experiences), *what are the most positive words you can say about yourself now? Imagine that person* (i.e., model or supportive figure) *standing near you and offering you what you need. Imagine that he or she knows exactly what to say to you, exactly what you need to hear. Imagine merging with this person or stepping right into his or her body. Imagine holding this resource* (i.e., a metaphoric or symbolic resource) *in your hands. Imagine being surrounded by this image or feeling. Breathe this feeling in. Notice where you feel the positive quality in your body.*

If possible, identify the positive belief and ask the client to say it during the pose.

8. Project the Resource into the Future

Think about possessing this resource in the future as you face ________ (describe the challenging situation identified earlier). *Imagine possessing the* ________ (e.g., courage, strength, boundaries) *you need to cope effectively. Imagine feeling* ________ (e.g., confident, peaceful, grounded) *in the scene. Imagine feeling connected with* ________ (name the client's supportive person or relational resource) *as you face this challenging situation. Notice what that would be like for you. Hear your resource person saying exactly what you need to hear. Feel your resource* (i.e., metaphoric or symbolic resources) *in just the way you need to feel it. Be aware of your resource in just the way you need to experience it.*

Continue with brief TAT poses or tapping, as long as there is a positive effect. Check whether the installation and the future projection with the selected resource help with the client's impression that he or she can do better in that situation. Ask: *Now, when you focus on* ________ (the problematic situation), *how true or supportive do you find* ________ (repeat the description of the image and feelings) *on a scale of 0 to 10, where 0 is completely false and unsupportive and 10 is completely true or supportive?*

This process can be repeated for each of the qualities that the client wants to strengthen.

9. Monitor Resources

In subsequent sessions, the therapist must reassess the resources installed to check whether they have remained stable. When the client is ready for the second phase of confrontation with the trauma, the therapist can start the session by asking the client to select the resources (installed previously or new ones) needed to face the trauma, and then reinforce them in the TAT pose or by tapping (e.g., by using Emotional Freedom Techniques [EFT] or Reed Eye Movement Acupressure Psychotherapy [REMAP]).

Resources can be reinforced by means of tapping on acupressure points while visualizing the associated scene. If negative elements appear during this reinforcement tapping (as expressed in thoughts, sensations, or negative emotions), they must be deactivated as they arise.

Therapists should also check whether this resource is always present and strongly anchored. If it is not, it can be reinforced by reinstalling it again and tapping and visualizing to strengthen it (Steps 7–9).

If the client is unable to find a resource, or if the resources cannot be maintained throughout treatment sessions, the therapist must check for the presence of the Self. In this context, the Self is the space within each person that is spontaneously serene and filled with compassion. It has no intention other than being.

Richard Schwartz's (1995) Internal Family Systems (IFS) model identifies eight qualities of the Self (the 8 C's):

- Calmness: comprising appeasement and composure
- Curiosity: the ability to welcome anything or hear anything
- Compassion: the ability to resonate with the experience of the other without being over identified
- Clarity: characterized by perceptiveness, clear vision
- (Self-) Confidence: trust in one's capabilities and skills
- Creativity: the drive to seek alternatives and new solutions
- Courage: the ability to move forward, to expose oneself
- Connectivity: the tendency to connect with others and with one's internal parts.

The qualities of the Self are always there, even after multiple traumas. The Self may be represented outside the body, and may appear to be hidden or damaged, and may also be denied, or repressed, but it is always there. Its knowledge and competence are always intact, and one simply has to allow for the natural flow of the Self. There is a spontaneous motivation to be healthy, for the Self is a natural healer. And it is also the natural leader of the internal psychological system, which establishes harmony. The Self's curiosity and compassion are highly useful to the therapist.

When we talk to clients, we seek to communicate with their Self. If the Self is present, there is flow, and there are no barriers to communication. Otherwise, another part of the psyche may manifest and block the treatment process. We can then metaphorically converse with this part and ask it to move aside for a while. In this process, we ask clients to focus inward and report their responses to questions directed toward any parts of their psyche that has appeared during the therapeutic process. For example, if the client becomes angry or sad, we directs our questions to the angry or sad parts of the client to ascertain how to proceed and help the client resolve the issues.

To check whether you are connected with the client's Self, the key is to ask, *"What do you feel for this part?"* If the client's response includes the eight qualities of the Self (compassion, calmness, confidence, etc.), then you have connected with the Self. Otherwise, it is a part of the client's psyche that is reacting. If there is a particular intention to do something, you are dealing with a part.

Example of Work Session on Resources

The objectives of the session are to install a resource or allow access to that peaceful and calm inner space—the Self (as it is called in IFS or Logosynthesis).

Yves: I would like you to think again about the angry part.

Céline: It's all me.

Yves: What do you feel for her?

This question is of major importance because it will allow us to differentiate between the various parts that are expressing (anger, controlling part, frustrated part, sad part, etc.) and the Self itself, which will express its owns qualities, the eight qualities of the Self—curiosity, compassion, creativity, calmness, etc.

Silence.

Céline: She pisses me off, because I am angry too at this angry part.

Yves: Okay. Could you tell her that you're angry at her and ask her what she needs?

Silence.

Céline: To cut the bond that makes me angry.

Yves: Is it more cut the bond or clean it?

Céline: It's complicated because I had the belief that cleaning was having a relationship with her and when I expressed my needs of hearing from her every 3 weeks, it went nowhere.

Yves: It's normal. Einstein said that if you start with the same things, you will get the same results.

Céline: But I changed. Before I was always yelling at her. Now I talked to her with empathy, but it didn't change a thing.

Yves: But you were still wanting the same thing.

Céline: Unconsciously, yes.

Yves: It's the whip, the stick....Repeat just that: "Even though a part of me was wanting her to change, I love and accept myself with my fragilities and my beliefs. A mother should love her child normally."

Céline repeats.

Céline: Normally, yes.

Yves: "Or not. On the other hand, I was a great person, even though I killed my cat. Actually, I did not kill the cat myself. I went away. I couldn't have saved my cat."

Céline repeats.

Céline: Actually, there were three more (laughing). They all died 6 months after my departure from the house.

Yves: You are a serial cat killer (laughing). I won't look at you the same way from now on. Have you tried dogs?

Céline: I Have a cat now.

Yves: Okay. "I open myself to the possibility of living in a different way."

Céline repeats.

Yves: Observe what happens.

Céline: It's bizarrely quiet.

Yves: Yes, bizarrely quiet. Weird....Mummy.

Céline: Oh my God.

Yves: Not my God. Mummy.

Silence.

Céline: I have the belief that I need to keep this anger.

Yves: Steve would say: "Of course, sure, 30 years at least."

Here, I am referring to Steve Reed, who developed the REMAP process.

Céline: No, it's enough.

Yves: Sure, 32 years?

Céline: No, 31 (laughing).

Yves (pretending to spit in his hand): Deal.

Yves: If you think back about the firemen, about your mother?

Céline: It's fairly quiet.

This is a sign that one of the big cores has been deactivated.

Céline: It's going to come back.

It is important to check whether the resource is holding. Here, I ask Céline to stimulate the meridian point Stomach 36 to prevent the issue from coming back.

Yves: So what kind of resource do you think you would need to be at peace?

Silence.

Yves: A baby dolphin? A boat full of dolphins? A massacre of dolphins? Something else?

Céline: I'm thinking. And I just saw the white chocolate Galak pack with the dolphin on it (laughing).

Yves: Oum? That's the name of the dolphin on the white chocolate Galak pack. A man?

Céline: I already have one.

Yves: Damn. So what would you need?

Céline: Actually to let go of this bond.

Yves: Is it true?

Céline: Yes.

Yves: Okay. What does it mean for you to let go of this bond?

Céline: Not think constantly about it, that it is like that and that's all.

Yves: You know there is a Belgian hero named Tintin.

Céline: It was my mother's favorite character (laughing).

Yves: No coincidences, it's the field. So in *The Blue Lotus,* there is a mad person with a sword and he runs after Tintin because Lao Tzu said that to find the way, he needed to cut off Tintin's head. If we cut off your head...

Céline: I'm in deep trouble.

Yves: And we put your husband's head instead...

Céline: Do you realize what you just said (laughing). Poor him.

Yves: Or you keep it or we can also put the cat's head. You choose (laughing) rare, medium, well done.

Céline: And the dog in the middle (laughing).

Yves: Hot dog (laughing). What resource would you need?

Céline: I don't know.

Yves: Imagine your mom. Look. I'm going to play a role. Dring, dring...

Silence.

Yves: You need to pick up.

Céline: It's not possible. She never phones.

Yves: We're playing a role. I push your point (GI 4).

Yves (in the mother's role): Hello, sweetie.

Céline: What do you want?

Yves (in the mother's role): Happy birthday.

Céline: It was 2 weeks ago.

Yves (in the mother's role): Happy non-birthday, happy non-birthday to you.

Yves: It's in Alice in Wonderland. You've got 364 non-birthdays and only one birthday. Think back about your mother. Dring Dring... (in the mother's role), hello, sweetie.

Céline: No, actually I believe that I don't pick up the phone.

Yves: Ahhh, this is letting go.

Céline: Yep.

Yves: Think back about this resource that you can say no.

Céline is laughing.

Céline: Difficult to say no.

Yves: Think about your husband.

Céline: To him, I always say no.

Yves: I was sure about that.

Céline: Poor him.

Yves: Facebook a little later (Céline laughs). Think back a little to the resource you would need to be able to set some rules and a limit.

Céline: I have no resource coming to mind, but...

Yves: Think about the last time that you said no to someone and not to me.

Céline: That's why I was looking (laughing).

Yves: I saw it in your eyes.

Céline: I did it not long ago, but I don't remember it.

Yves: Was it not about coffee?

Céline: Yes, I refused a job to respect myself.

Yves: Can you think about that?

Céline: I was under pressure.

Yves: But you did it and now how does it feel?

Céline: I'm happy.

Yves: So you are going to anchor this. Take that point (ear relaxation). I would like you to anchor that feeling.

Céline: Yes, I was very proud of myself.

Yves: Okay. Stimulate that, stay with the feeling, and think back a little about your mother and the firemen.

Céline: Something is coming up again, nausea again.

Yves: Stimulate this point (Pericardium 6: sadness and point to help calm nausea) What do you notice?

The important thing here is to find the right resource and to test it. This is why I asked Céline to think again about her mother and the firemen. As something is coming up again, it blocks the resource, even if the resource is a right one, so we need to clean what is polluting the resource. When we get a stronger level of resource, we can return to dealing with the trauma and its associated beliefs.

Yves: What do you notice?

Céline: It went down.

Yves: Okay. Come back to the resource, your pride in saying no.

Céline: No, it's coming up again.

Yves: Okay. What is coming up?

Céline: I cannot be proud of me.

Yves: Ahhh, that's another problem? What is it related to?

Céline: I don't know.

Yves: Okay. Could you tell this part that cannot be proud that I'm interested in knowing her better. Are there things she would like to share with me? What does she need to explain?

Silence.

Céline: She wants to say that it's not part of my values to be proud of me. I was never taught to. I was constantly reduced and criticized even when I had good marks at school.

We see clearly here that these are complex traumas with clear attachment disorders and many aspects are emerging. Here, the best thing to do is calm this part to be able to continue working with the resource that we need, to make it stronger. So the solution is to work on the Self's access first.

Yves: Could you repeat this to that part: "Even though I've never had the right to be proud of myself, it's not part of my values, I was never taught to, I was always criticized even if I had good marks at school. I cannot love and accept myself, but I open myself to the possibility to try. And there is another reality, it's that here and now, I can be proud to be in front of an audience, on the stage. It was not easy for me, even more as it is going to be on YouTube within an hour. And I open myself to the possibility to live things differently."

This is the five-part reframe.

Céline repeats it.

Yves: Simply notice what is happening.

Here I ask Céline to stimulate the ear relaxation point: anxiety, trauma.

Céline: I believe that 2 years ago, I wouldn't have been on the stage.

Yves: What do you feel in your body?

Céline: It's very quiet.

Yves: Okay. Think a little about this resource of having the power to say no and to feel okay with it. How do you feel now?

Céline: It's weird; there is nothing anymore.

Yves: Think back about the situation with your mother (*I ask Céline to change to the ear relaxation point on the other side*), the firemen.... How do you feel now?

Céline: Very quiet.

Yves: Okay. Think a little now about....Dring dring. Oh, it's Mummy.

This is to check whether the situation will be okay in future occurrences too.

Céline: I think that I would need to know what to do, without ruining my life ever again. I would love to have a ready solution that would be right for me.

I pick up a bottle and balance it in front of Céline (laughing).

Yves: Imagine that this is a crystal ball. You can call me Madam Irma (covering the bottle with a tissue and rubbing it like a crystal ball as if to look into it and predict the future).

Yves: I see that you can do it—a 10 life from here, maybe 9. It depends, if you stop eating all that chocolate and stop smoking cigarettes.

Céline (smiling): It's funny.

Yves: For me, yes. Think a little about dring dring dring...how do you feel?

Céline: I start to understand that even though I love to anticipate things, seeing all the possibilities...

I hold the bottle with the tissue on top of it in front of Céline again.

Céline (laughing): Maybe the police will call me.

Yves: Maybe.

Céline: Or maybe not.

Yves: Okay. How do you feel?

Céline (smiling): I feel good.

Yves: Mummy. Miaou (imitating a cat; Céline laughs). What sensation do you feel? Think about the situation from the beginning.

Céline: Everything is okay.

Yves (being ironic and smiling): What am I going to do with you? It's not possible.

Céline: It's peculiar.

Yves: Okay. Then I thank you, Céline.

Céline: Thank you.

A few months after our work together, Céline changed her life in a new and happy way. Now, a year later she is pregnant (she had previously been unable to conceive, despite several years of medical treatment).

If the Self is not accessible, it will be necessary to work temporarily via the therapist's Self. If the therapeutic relationship is sound enough, this Self will be the one through which the client will be able to hear what he might have felt and recognized. And from this recognition or reconnection, the therapist should be able gradually to link the client to his own Self and, from there, continue the reconstruction and freeing of this space that all individuals have within themselves. In practice, this means that, from her Self, the therapist will express what she feels for those of the client's parts that are present and, in this way, seek to reconnect the client with his own Self.

This round about way should ideally be temporary, for the idea is not to risk an unhealthy transference from the client to the therapist, but instead to use the transference relationship in a beneficial way so that the client can reconnect with himself, and thus with that internal space of serenity of the Self.

If this does not happen, it is first necessary to verify the quality of the therapeutic relationship and to enhance it through better therapist-client communication. In this case, client-centered, Rogerian approaches can be used.

The therapist can also suggest that the client use various self-help techniques between sessions, such as self-hypnosis, meditation, Energy Psychology techniques, and mindfulness. This will enable the therapist to ensure that the client's resources are properly installed and that the Self is present, for if the client is able to do this work, it means that the Self is present and free. If the client is not yet able to do so, the therapist must first verify the Self and proceed with reinforcing the resources, before anything else. When the resources are strong and firmly rooted, the client will begin taking care of himself.

There are ways of checking whether the treatment is working and whether the benefits of the sessions are becoming part of the client's daily experience. You can use the SUD scale to determine whether the session is working or control the next session if something changed in the client's life or the "thema" (e.g., belief) changed.

If the Self is present and accessible, the therapist can start looking for a trigger in the present. First, identify the negative cognition in order to identify a positive cognition, that is, a resource, to install or reinforce. From there, alternate between reinforcing the resource and desensitizing the trigger.

When enough triggers in the present are deactivated, attention can then turn to events from the past. Depending on the client's sensitivity, it is advisable to start from the least traumatic events in the past and work toward the most traumatic ones that trigger the strongest reactions. If the Self and the resources are sufficiently present, the therapist can try to work directly on a sensitive or difficult event from the past. If in doubt, first look for "lighter" events from the past to check the stability of the resources and the presence of the Self.

Often people don't understand the effect of provocative style or the strength of the presence, the Self of the therapist, or the importance of accessing the Self of the client. So I asked Céline to give me an inside perspective on the session because she would have different observations on: the voice, the support, the good will, but also the provocation coming from me and the acupressure point. The audience would likewise have different observations: the quality of the alliance, the verbal therapy, the exchanges, the provocation, the time, the request for stimulating different acupressure points. As an observer of the process, I wanted to hear how it felt to Céline.

Céline answered that there were some silent moments, then when she was asked to focus on what is happening in her body in the REMAP process, it was really physical and, with the acupressure points, she felt it inside her body. Yves kept silent as things were changing inside her body. The sensations increased or decreased, and he just had her change to different points according to the emotion that emerged. She felt the change inside.

What is important to notice is that the process works on its own and we need to let it do so because an intervention will only slow down the process or return the people who are very mental to their cognition, which we don't want.

The approach of the treatment plan is thus the opposite to that of simple traumas.

When you start working, it is essential to start from a present trigger and check whether there is sufficient accessibility to the Self. Afterward you apply this oscillation and resource installation in order to desensitize the chosen target. For a memory, the target must be composed of: a real situation with an image (the worse image), the sensations, the emotions, and a belief (the main belief associated with the situation). When you have sufficiently desensitized the target in the present, you can start working step by step on the events and targets from the past in order to free the client completely, if that is the client's request.

If the subject is highly sensitive, it is also possible to use an eye-movement treatment (e.g., REMAP, Eye Movement Desensitization and Reprocessing [EMDR], or eye-movement integration) to accelerate or slow down the process and help keep the client within the zone of comfort where it is possible to work. This will avoid unnecessary discomfort for the client and will ensure that no abreaction or dissociation occurs.

If the client tends to dissociate or intellectualize, I advise that the therapist first verify the presence of a space of security and the presence of or access to the Self, because dissociation is a defense mechanism. If the subconscious has deemed dissociation necessary, it is for a good reason. So the therapist must proceed with caution and ensure that all steps are carried out to verify a space of security and the presence of resources or the accessibility of the Self.

Once these preliminary steps have been taken, therapists can ask clients to tell their stories or share their feelings by acting out or through gentle provocation, linking the event to the emotions that it is normal to feel in such cases. Paul Gilbert (2010a), in his book *Compassion Focused Therapy,* advises the therapist to mirror the client's emotions. This process provides a gateway that can facilitate reconnection. When the therapist sees that the client is reconnecting with her emotions, the next step is to check for the presence of negative sensations, emotions, and cognition.

Caution should be taken in cases of complex trauma: It may be useful to divide the anamnesis into several parts to ensure that the client is not triggered too strongly. It is usually better not to stimulate any acupressure points during the anamnesis. When patients shift very quickly from abreaction to dissociation and vice versa, however, the stimulation of acupoints sometimes amplifies the effect of resonance and aids the reconnection while maintaining the zone of comfort needed to work (see the two-part videos demonstrating this process: http://www.youtube.com/watch?v=bKWtfVdS-Rw and http://www.youtube.com/watch?v=Rkw_Dm9rdwo).

Remember that, in a case of trauma, it is important to avoid asking for details; the first step is to stabilize the client (mainly by reframing) and then integrate the memories using Energy Psychology techniques such as EFT and REMAP. Finally, in the third phase, the growth and development of the significance of the event and the ability to move toward the future are added.

If the subject is so sensitive that the client has an emotionally overwhelming reaction at the slightest reference to his situation, it is better to work directly on the Self, the space of security, the envisioned container, and the client's resources. The therapeutic relationship is obviously also a guarantor of the maintenance of this zone of comfort.

In the case of very strong reactions, the therapist should immediately consider stimulating acupressure points such as those of Quick REMAP (Large Intestine 4, Stomach 36, Ear relax point, Extra point 1—but it is important to remember that LI4 and S36 are not recommended for pregnant women; the location of these points is demonstrated in a short video by the author at http://www.youtube.com/watch?v=QMVfSKngPO0). In such a situation, the therapist should aim to bring the client back to the here and now, with his eyes open, getting him to focus on objects surrounding him and talking to him calmly and firmly. The therapist may also use reframing techniques, such as REMAP, in which the client is guided through a process of self-acceptance, by articulating the following series of statements:

1. "Even though I have _______" (this problem; be specific)...
2. "I completely accept myself" (or "I am open to the possibility of deeply accepting myself")...
3. "And it is normal, logical, or natural that I feel...(a phrase describing this feeling)."
4. "On the other hand, another reality is that..." (Use a real, verified positive element, for example, "it's over and I'm safe here and now.")
5. "I am simply open to the possibility of being able to digest and manage these things differently" (or "to be at peace with this").

When I talk about the process of reframing, people are often intrigued that I mix the part about acceptance—"I love myself, I do not love myself"—with saying, "There is a situation...and in the meantime, there is another situation..." They ask me if it is a real REMAP or just something I add.

In the first place, this is part of the reframing in REMAP and EFT, but Steve Reed deals a lot less with complex trauma with attachment disorders. Therefore, if we reframe following the classical process in REMAP or EFT, which is "Even though I have this problem, I love and I accept myself (step 2), but in reality I'm here on the stage (step 3)," it does not work here. You can try, but the parts are so much in opposition that if you say, for example, "Even though I almost died in that building and I hate my mother, I love and accept myself..." it won't work.

So I have built a reframing in five steps. The first two are the same you use in EFT or REMAP: "Even though I have this problem, I love and accept myself." The third one is the recognition of what is happening, so the parts that have not been recognized until now can be heard as they need to be heard. So just say to them: "It's normal that I am completely angry at this worthy mother that I hate." This way, the parts feel heard and calm down. There is, however, one particularity in step 4, which you can check, at the right moment, in reference to the event/problem: "In reality, I was a great child and I am a great person now." It means: "I am not a hateful person, even though I did not receive all the love I needed." The fact that we introduce a real element allows the person to connect the resource to the system. We don't want to close the unconscious, as the unconscious knows better than we do. Therefore, at this step, we open the possibility and present it in general terms—"I open myself to the possibility of living things in a different way, of being able to feel things differently, of being able to breathe and feel freedom." Presenting it in general terms allows the unconscious do its job. As we introduce this real element, the unconscious searches the positive elements and finds what we as practitioners could not possibly identify. Therapists who have tried this five-point reframing method tell me it is very helpful and has changed their way of working.

Conclusion

The therapist should keep in mind that dissociation and abreaction are defense mechanisms that suggest that work should proceed cautiously. It is also important to remember to check any possible medical aspects of the client's condition. If you as the therapist have the slightest doubt as to the client's state of health (as indicated, e.g., by the client's symptoms), advise the client to consult a medical practitioner or mental health specialist.

Working via the Self is essential, as it will enable the therapist to install or reinstall the space of security. Note that in the case of children or adults who have experienced early childhood trauma, the first thing to do is to stabilize them and then to create a space of security within a safe therapeutic relationship.

Finally, therapists should remember that if they are not comfortable with a "complex trauma" client, they should seek immediate supervision or refer the client to a colleague who is more experienced in this respect. Our main concern must be to deal with the client's needs in a safe and integrated manner.

References

Church, D. (2013). *The EFT manual* (3rd ed.). Santa Rosa, CA: Energy Psychology Press.

Gallo, F. P. & Vincenzi, H. (2008). *Energy tapping: How to rapidly eliminate anxiety, depression, cravings, and more using energy psychology* (2nd ed.). Oakland, CA: New Harbinger.

Gilbert, P. (2010a). *Compassion focused therapy: Distinctive features.* New York, NY: Routledge.

Gilbert, P. (2010b). *The compassionate mind: A new approach to life's challenges.* Oakland, CA: New Harbinger.

Hansoul, B. & Wauthier, Y. (2010). *EFT, tapping, and energy psychology*. Labege, France: Edition Dangles.

Korn, D. L. & Leeds, A. M. (2002). Preliminary evidence for efficacy for EMDR: Resource development and installation in the stabilization phase of treatment of complex post-traumatic stress disorder. *Journal of Clinical Psychology, 58*, 1465–1487.

Lammers, W. (2009). *Phrases to freedom: Self-coaching with Logosynthesis* (P. Cooney, Trans.). Charleston, SC: BookSurge.

Leeds, A M. (2009). A guide to the standard EMDR protocols for clinicians, supervisors, and consultants. New York, NY: Springer.

Mémoire traumatique et victimologie [Traumatic Memory and Victimology]. (n.d.). Psychotraumatismes. Retrieved from http://memoiretraumatique.org/psychotraumatismes/generalites.html

O'Shea, M. K. & Paulsen, S. L. (2007, September). *A protocol for increasing affect regulation and clearing early trauma.* Paper presented at the annual meeting of the Eye Movement Desensitization and Reprocessing International Association Conference, Dallas, TX.

Paul, G. (2010a). *Compassion focused therapy: Distinctive features.* New York, NY: Routledge.

Paul, G. (2010b). *The compassionate mind: A new approach to life's challenges.* Oakland, CA: New Harbinger.

Schwartz, R. C. (1995). *Internal family systems therapy.* New York, NY: Guilford Press.

Shapiro, R. (Ed.). (2009). *EMDR solutions II: For depression, eating disorders, performance, and more.* New York, NY: W. W. Norton.

Van der Hart, O., Nijenhuis, E., & Steele, K. (2006). *The haunted self: Structural dissociation and the treatment of chronic traumatization.* New York, NY: W. W. Norton.

REVIEW ARTICLE

The Energetics of Group Trance: New Research, Applications, and Implications

Eric Leskowitz, Harvard Medical School

Abstract

The phenomenon of hypnotic trance is generally conceptualized in the interpersonal context of the therapeutic relationship between therapist and patient. However, group trance is a widely recognized phenomenon whose power may stem from intangible and invisible forces that resemble Franz Mesmer's 200-year-old notion of "animal magnetism." Technological detection systems can now study this force and are here discussed: in the laboratory, emotional contagion has been monitored by measuring heart rate variability; in the larger setting of a baseball stadium, group-focused attention has been monitored by random number generators. Such studies are beginning to validate the transpersonal model of hypnosis, in which human consciousness is seen as extending beyond the boundaries of the individual personality and brain.

Keywords: hypnosis, transpersonal, trance, subtle energy, electromagnetic field, EMF, heart rate variability, HRV, random number generator

Eric Leskowitz, MD, is a psychiatrist in practice at Spaulding Rehabilitation Hospital, Harvard Medical School. **Correspondence:** PO Box 92, Buckland MA 01338; e-mail: eleskowitz@partners.org. **Disclosure:** The author declares no conflicts of interest.

Introduction

The standard model of clinical hypnosis explains trance as an interactive phenomenon that is mediated by verbal interchanges involving one or more of the five physical senses to initiate a cascade of changes in brain function. These changes create an altered state of consciousness that is conducive to modifications in behavior. The transpersonal model of hypnosis proposes that human beings can interact at a distance via mechanisms that extend beyond the five physical senses, with consciousness existing independent of the brain. Scientific data (Tart, 1975, 2009) suggest that consciousness exists as a continuum extending beyond the brain; in this model, the brain does not produce consciousness so much as act like a radio receiver or filter. Consciousness may thereby generate anomalous or paranormal experiences that go beyond the personality (hence *trans*personal) in scope. Walsh and Vaughan (1993) define transpersonal as "experiences in which the sense of identity or self extends beyond (trans) the individual or personal to encompass wider aspects of humankind, life, psyche, and cosmos" (p. 3).

This article will focus on group interactions as one forum in which these unusual phenomena can be reliably experienced, and will address the role of the element often referred to as "group energy" as a possible mediating factor in synchronized group behaviors. Finally, the concept of electromagnetic and psychospiritual energies as bridges to the transpersonal realm will be related to the practice of hypnosis, to the clinician-patient relationship in general, and to the wide range of coordinated group processes in human and animal behavior.

Group Behaviors

Human beings have always been fascinated by the power of group processes, whether at music concerts, religious ceremonies, political rallies, or sporting events, and the manipulation of these energies lies at the root of many great cultural and political movements (Ehrenreich, 2006). Early Greek and Roman civilizations were both marked by ritual celebrations that triggered enthusiastic, if not frenzied participation—the Bacchanals and the cult of Dionysius, to name two. In medieval times, group dancing was so popular that it was perceived as a threat to the dominance of feudal authorities and was actually outlawed in some jurisdictions (Ehrenreich, 2006). Mob psychology was a powerful force in WWII Germany (Shirer, 1941), where Hitler's infamous Nuremberg rallies exemplified his ability to catalyze powerful group energies, vividly captured in Leni Riefenstahl's film *Triumph of Will.* More recently, group hysteria among highly suggestible subpopulations has been proposed as the cause of the apparently contagious spread of psychophysiological symptoms such as fainting and laughter in noninfectious epidemics (Moss & McEvedy, 1966).

Complementing these sociological studies, neuroscientists have highlighted the role of subcortical mirror neurons in facilitating emotional contagion, the dynamic spread of behaviors such as laughter and yawning (Haker, Kawohl, Herwig, & Rössler, 2013). Surprisingly, the scientific study of group phenomena is not new, and can be traced to the work of 18th century Austrian physician Franz Mesmer, best known for his concept of animal magnetism. Mesmer is often referred to as the father of hypnosis (Ellenberger, 1970), and the word "mesmerized" is used colloquially as a synonym for "hypnotized." However, Mesmer's intervention differed significantly from the verbal interactions that characterize modern clinical hypnosis. His primary explanatory element, the invisible vital force of animal magnetism, is absent from the conceptual portfolio of modern Western medicine, and more closely parallels the Chinese concept of "qi" and the yoga concept of "prana" (Feinstein, 2012). Mesmer's work has typically been dismissed as quackery, in part because a French Royal Commission that convened in 1789 to investigate his work harshly criticized his methods (Gauld, 1992). But contemporary science is now validating many of his central concepts by using modern technology to measure such aspects of animal magnetism as the human electromagnetic field (Green, 1992).

Mesmer's clinical work in Paris in the 1780s made use of group interactions, in part because his individual practice was expanding so rapidly that this logistical change was necessary to accommodate his ever-growing (and wealthy) clientele (Winter, 1998). He assembled large clusters of patients around a wooden basin filled with "magnetized" water that he had previously energized by charging it with his own personal animal magnetism. This device to store his energy was modeled after the Leyden jar, an electrical capacitor invented in 1745 that was the precursor of the modern storage battery (Ellenberger, 1970); its presence lent an aura of scientific credibility to his methods. Each patient could then partake of Mesmer's healing energy by touching one of the iron rods protruding from the basin. The beneficial impact of this contact would spread throughout the room in a wave of contagious symptom release (fainting spells, spasmodic movements, and verbal outbursts) called mass hysteria by his critics but known to his adherents as healing crises.

Today these behaviors would be considered evidence of group trance induction, because Mesmer skillfully (if unknowingly) capitalized on his patients' suggestibility by using such additional nonspecific trance-induction factors as his own celebrity and charismatic personality, his exotic and attention-grabbing robe and cap, a semi-darkened treatment room, and ethereal background music played on the glass harmonica (Ellenberger, 1970). In any case, the idea that a collective gathering could generate a powerful beneficial impact on a subject was well known over 200 years ago.

The Royal Commission rejected the existence of animal magnetism, and instead invoked the power of suggestion as the underlying healing power. This was perhaps the first official medical acknowledgment that the power of suggestion in and of itself can influence one's health. In so doing, the Royal Commission effectively stigmatized any future clinical investigation of electromagnetic phenomena for over 100 years, while giving impetus to the study of psychological factors such as suggestion in health and illness, thereby paving the way for mind-body medicine and modern clinical hypnosis.

Animal Magnetism and Electromagnetism

However, with the advent of sophisticated electronic recording instruments in the 20th century, "animal magnetism" has found renewed credibility in its incarnation as the science of biomagnetism. It is a well-founded and well-researched field, with professional societies, journals, and conferences, studying applications ranging from human behavioral interactions (Ravitz, 1959) and other animal behavior (e.g., homing pigeons; Cavagna et al., 2010) to intracellular regulatory processes (Gartzke & Lange, 2002). Of relevance for this discussion, an electromagnetic field (EMF) surrounds living things (Figure 1), and the human EMF extends several feet beyond the skin. The latter EMF has been well characterized, and will be

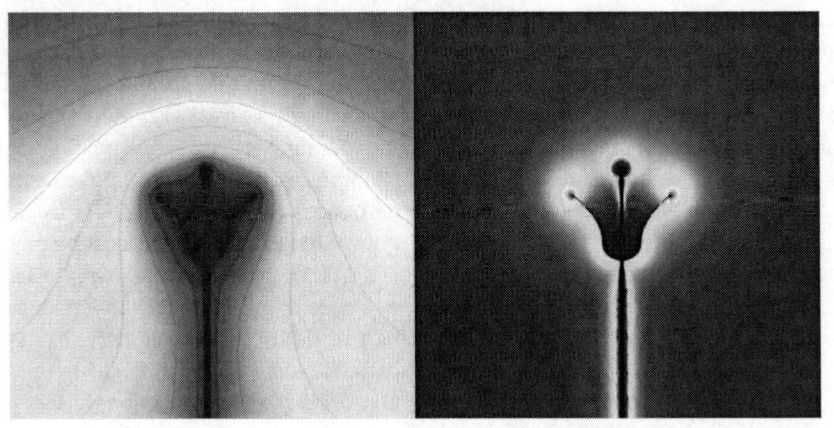

Figure 1. EMF surrounding a flower.

proposed as a possible mechanism that helps coordinate synchronized group interactions by linking large arrays of people together.

The heart has the strongest and most extensive magnetic field of any organ in the human body, readily detectible up to 3 feet away (Figure 2; McCraty, 2004). Cardiologists have long known that the heart does not beat as regularly as a metronome; rather, the interval between beats varies in a pattern that depends on many factors including, most importantly, one's emotional state. Anger or frustration produces erratic but not wide-ranging variations in heart rate, while emotions such as appreciation produce the large amplitude sinusoidal alterations in heart rate known as sinus arrhythmia; this rhythm is indicative of a balance between the sympathetic and parasympathetic branches of the autonomic nervous system. The index for monitoring these variations is called heart rate variability (HRV). The heart rate in frustration varies erratically, while in relaxation it varies in a rhythmically ordered manner. A second-order mathematical derivative of HRV called heart coherence has been developed by researchers at the Institute of HeartMath (IHM), and is only elicited by positive emotions like appreciation, not by simple mental or physical relaxation exercises (Figure 3; from Childre and Martin, 1999).

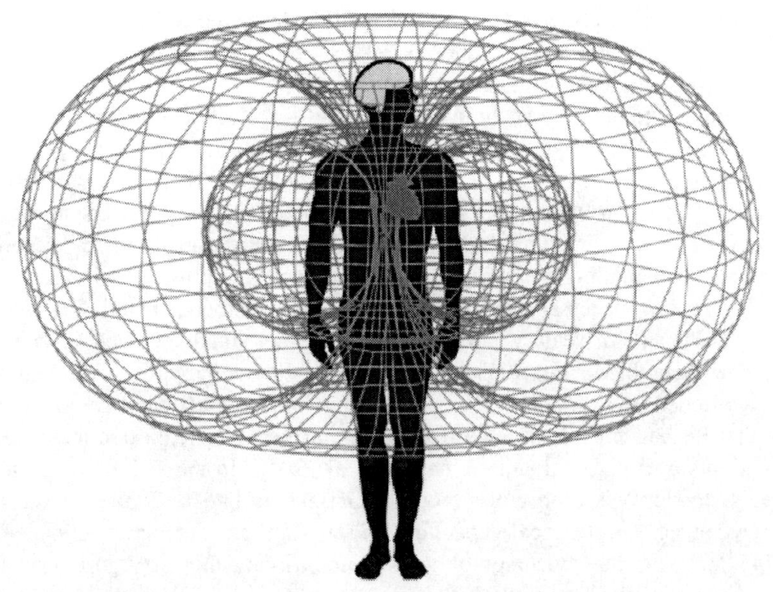

Figure 2. The heart's EMF.

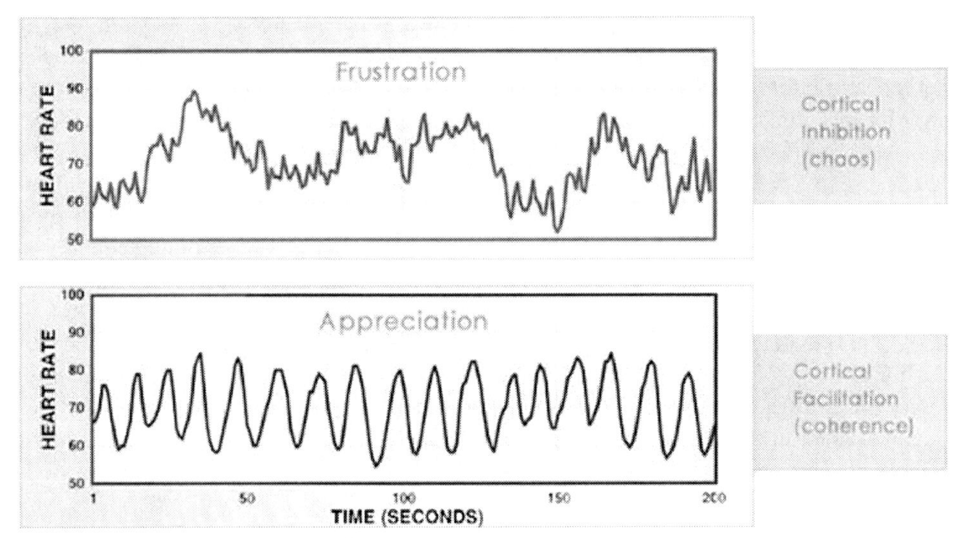

Figure 3. HRV in frustration and appreciation.

Importantly, individuals in this state of elevated heart coherence have a higher degree of mind-body coordination than in other states, and this state enhances physiological and behavioral performance (Tiller, McCraty, & Atkinson, 1996). For example, athletes have been shown to improve reflex response time significantly, reacting up to 37 milliseconds more quickly (McCraty, Atkinson, & Bradley, 2004). IHM researcher Rollin McCraty has stated that this beneficial psychophysiological effect of heart coherence allows a baseball batter facing a 90-mile-per-hour fastball to perceive it as moving only at 80 mph, due to his heightened reflexes (Leskowitz & Leskowitz, 2012). Hence, any practice that increases an athlete's heart coherence will enhance his or her coordination and performance levels.

Heart Coherence

IHM developed a standardized three-step technique to maximize heart coherence called HeartLock (Childre and Martin, 1999). First, positive feelings and memories are recalled in as much multisensorial depth as possible. Then an imaginary flow of breath is directed in and out of the heart area of the sternum. And finally, these feelings are projected outward to other people. While its developers do not consider the technique to be a form of trance induction, the role of internal imagery and fixed attentional focus here is clearly hypnotic in nature. Researchers have speculated that the rhythmic oscillation of the cardiac component of the human EMF may account for the interpersonal and interactive aspects of emotional states, and may underlie the previously mentioned phenomenon of emotional contagion, both positive, as in church congregations and concerts, and negative, as in mobs (Tatum, 1999).

An important heuristic tool for understanding this group phenomenon is the image of resonance, with one evocative metaphor comparing people's emotions to tuning forks (Tatum, 1999). For example, if someone is emotionally "vibrating" at the frequency of anger, anyone else in proximity will begin to experience this same emotion when his or her own emotional tuning fork begins to resonate in empathy. Positive emotions like joy can also vibrate in harmony, setting up standing waves that develop a self-sustaining autonomy via the process known in physics as sympathetic resonance (Tiller, in Leskowitz & Leskowitz, 2012).

This intriguing way of describing how people can affect each other by interacting at a distance also suggests another perspective for understanding commonly experienced phenomena like empathy, emotional contagion, and hypnotic trance induction. All may involve a mechanism that researchers in biomagnetism have explored, positing that the EMF surrounding each person may be susceptible to resonant entrainment with other nearby EMFs (McCraty, 2004). In one study (Bair, 2008), the heart rates of subjects receiving energy healing were found to synchronize with those of the nearby healer (HRV was not tested). In another, a dog's heart rhythm became entrained to his owner's heart rhythm when the owner entered the room (McCraty, 2004).

Resonance in the Lab

These interpersonal effects can be measured and recorded in the psychophysiology laboratory. I recently served as a subject in one such study (Leskowitz, 2009) to determine whether the EMF generated by a group of heart coherence adepts could affect a nearby subject. As the naïve subject, I was untrained in the HeartLock technique and was sitting in sensory isolation, with my eyes blindfolded and my ears plugged. I entered a light trance state via simple progressive muscle relaxation and diaphragmatic breathing, but according to subsequent analysis of the heart rate monitor, this process did not generate a significant degree of heart coherence. However, when a small group of trained HeartLock practitioners entered the room, sat behind me (unbeknownst to me), and began to generate their own distinct cardiac rhythm simply by focusing on an internal emotional state of appreciation, my nervous system responded with a prompt and dramatic increase in heart coherence, a shift I hadn't been able to create intentionally when relaxing in isolation (Figure 4).

Interestingly, a classic hypnotic suggestibility effect is not likely to explain the dramatic shift in my own physiology during the test, since I was given no direct suggestion for a psychophysiological response, as is typically done in hypnotic induction protocols. While waiting for the HeartMath practitioners to enter the room, I had already entered a state of self-induced relaxation, marked by an attitude of hopeful expectancy but without specific goals or conceptual understanding of the physiology of inducing heart coherence. I was unaware of when the HeartMath practitioners initiated their self-hypnotic internal focus since I was blinded to the experimenter's cue for them to begin, yet my physiology responded within seconds to their shift in consciousness—again, without any direct cueing perceivable by me.

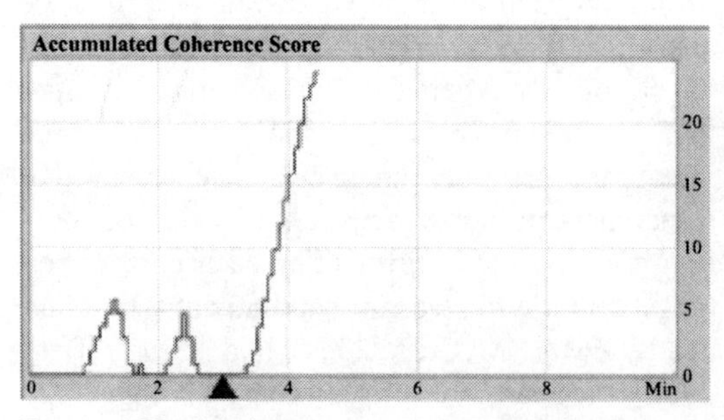

Figure 4. Heart coherent response to group intent.

I am proposing that my physiological shift resulted from the resonant interaction of adjacent EMFs, in what would be a reconceptualized manifestation of animal magnetism. It is less likely, but not inconceivable, that in my light trance state, my unconscious mind was somehow able to respond to changes in the internal mental activity of the adjacent participants. While some experimental data validating this type of anomalous cognition or transpersonal information flow (i.e., telepathic communication) do exist (Radin, 2006), consideration of this topic is beyond the scope of this paper.

The collective field of these practitioners may have entrained my nervous system, outside of my conscious awareness, to resonate in alignment with theirs, as in the tuning fork analogy. And if four appreciative people could generate an effect strong enough to influence me, what would happen with 25 highly focused people in a classroom, or 2,000 singing fans in a concert hall, or 35,000 cheering fans in a baseball stadium, or millions of compassionately aligned people across the globe? The latter is being explored by the Global Coherence Initiative, a collaboration among IHM, the Institute of Noetic Sciences (IONS), and other groups exploring the nature of consciousness and distant intentionality (www.glcoherence.org).

The Home Field Advantage

During the lab demonstration just described, I was presumably lifted into a state of greater mind-body coordination by virtue of the coherent influence of the shared group trance state. Similarly, appreciative fans may unwittingly lift musicians or athletes into "the Zone" of peak performance via the entraining impact of their coordinated resonant group energy field. This intangible process may be an unrecognized contributor to the home field advantage (HFA) that is widely recognized in competitive sports, and which ranges in impact from a 53% victory rate in home baseball games to 57% in football, and over 60% in soccer (Jamieson, 2010). The HFA is usually attributed to such concrete factors as absence of jet lag, home cooking, cheers of support from the hometown fans, and even the design of new stadiums (Watson & Krantz, 2003) but may also owe some of its potency to the indirect impact of the EMFs generated by the group's strong attentional focus. In other words, fans who are in this shared trance state (i.e., are more fully "entranced" by their team) could potentially help their team outperform opponents with more blasé fans.

A similar resonance process may underlie a phenomenon that often occurs at conferences and professional meetings where clinical demonstrations of novel therapies are presented. During many years of attending meetings of the American Society of Clinical Hypnosis (ASCH), I have yet to see an unsuccessful demonstration of a hypnotic treatment intervention, no matter how unusual the symptom or the technique. The statistical validity of this uncontrolled observation would of course be strengthened by follow-up information on the status of the subjects 3 months after the conference. It's likely that the highly supportive atmosphere at these sessions plays a role in increasing the success rate by maximizing expectancy factors and role conformation pressure in the subjects. But at ASCH, where an appreciative audience generates a coherent energy field that entrains the demonstration subjects (and the hypnosis practitioners), this audience effect may parallel the HFA process by which sports fans elevate the performance level of their hometown favorites by lifting them into the Zone. Perhaps hypnotherapists and their subjects are also susceptible to a "home field advantage" that may be mediated by these same intangible forces.

Animal Behavior

A related group phenomenon is the animal behavior known as schooling. The highly coordinated flight of a flock of birds (called a murmuration) and the swimming of a school of fish have generated several theories to explain these highly synchronized group behaviors. A mechanistic cognitive model posits that there is in fact a lead fish or bird, and the other group members are simply responding to visual and auditory cues to adapt their behavior to their leader's changes in direction and velocity.

In this vein, "scale-free correlation" is a computer modeling system that describes the morphology of flock behavior accurately (Cavagna et al., 2010). However, the lag time involved in neuronal information processing and transfer across large numbers of unit animals renders this mechanism implausible because it requires a nearly instantaneous and flawless information transfer among the members of the flock—a process for which there is no known physiological mechanism. Videos of flocking behavior illustrate the precise coordination of these behaviors and show that the timing is too precise and well synchronized to be reactive (vimeo.com/58291553).

While the principles of hypnosis may not apply to animal behavior, a nonmaterial organizational structure called a morphic field has been proposed (Sheldrake, 1995) as the mediator of this supraordinal level of control. Morphic fields may be mediated by EMFs, which are known to underlie such aspects of animal behavior as directional orientation (Wiltschko & Wiltschko, 1995; Giller, 2014) and group alignment (Begall, Cerveny, Neef, Vojtech, & Burda, 2008).

Random Number Generators

Another relevant and innovative measurement technique is also more controversial, because the results it generates suggest that human thought can directly alter nonliving physical or mechanical systems. Researchers at the Princeton Engineering Anomalies Research (PEAR) lab at Princeton University use a random number generator (RNG) to detect changes in human consciousness (their research studies can be accessed at www.princeton.edu/~pear). Surprisingly, a computer that electronically generates a random string of 1s or 0s (in essence, digitally flipping a coin a thousand times a second) will show, under certain circumstances, a statistically significant perturbation from the expected 50:50 distribution of these 1s and 0s. Focused human intention in the laboratory can reliably alter this stream of data, and while the absolute size of this impact is small, the consistent replication of these results over thousands of trials has raised this effect to the level of statistical certainty.

Non-Newtonian explanations for this mind-machine interaction are required, and thus have been difficult to conceptualize, with quantum entanglement of consciousness being one possible mechanism (Dossey, 2007). Portable RNG units developed by the Global Consciousness Project (noosphere.princeton.edu) allow measurements

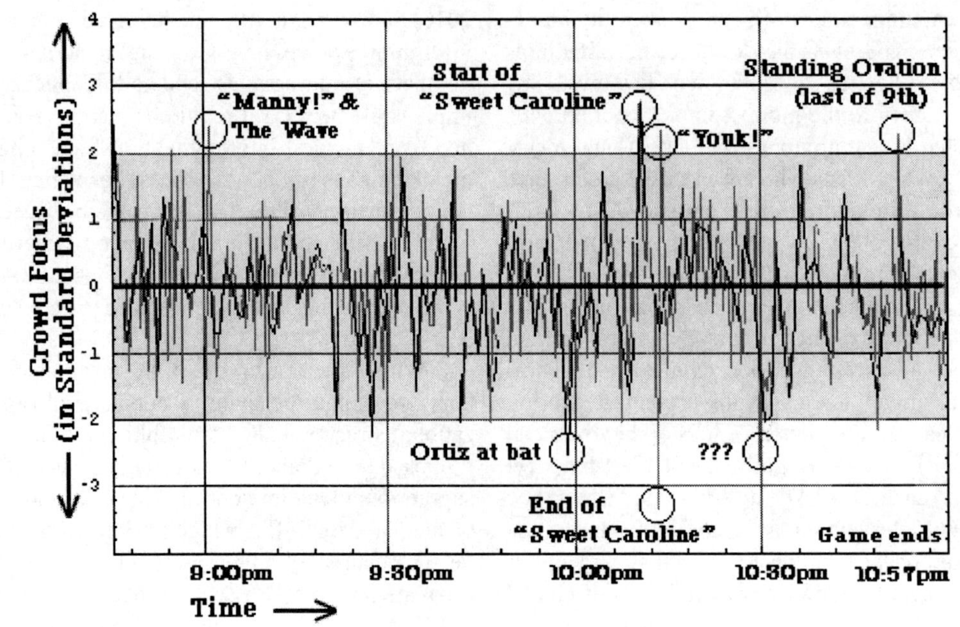

Figure 5. RNG measurements during a baseball game.

to be taken in the field as well as in the laboratory. RNG readings taken at the ballpark by the author during the course of a professional baseball game (Leskowitz, 2011) showed that the moments of highest levels of RNG nonrandomness (as revealed by subsequent analysis of the RNG data stream) were concurrent with moments that had been independently and subjectively judged to have the highest degree of emotional intensity or significance to the game (i.e., rallies, home runs, cheers). In fact, the odds that this correspondence between statistically significant RNG peaks and important game events was random exceeded 1:10,000.

Two moments of coordinated crowd behavior generated the strongest response in the RNG software. The "Wave" is a synchronized standing and cheering movement that travels around the stadium in a wavelike pattern, and its spontaneous emergence partway through the game created the second largest RNG impact during the game. Interestingly, given Mesmer's historical precedent of using music to maximize suggestibility, and given research describing the beneficial impact of music on the hypnotic process (Kelly, 1993), the game moment marked by the most statistically significant shift in RNG output (3.40 standard deviations from baseline, with 2.0 SD being the threshold of statistical significance) occurred during a regularly scheduled, and wildly popular, sing-along to the classic rock song "Sweet Caroline" (Figure 5).

During the sing-along, physical movement, emotional arousal, and melodic entrainment were key elements in eliciting this group trance state, one of high enough coherence to register on the RNG device. Similarly, a genre of electronic dance music called "trance music" uses a rapid beat and repetitive melodic phrases to entrain participants into a group trance state of shared euphoria. RNG recordings have not been made in this setting but would be predicted to show high levels of response.

RNG measurements have been taken to determine whether detectable vibratory activity remains after a significant event has concluded, a project inspired by the common subjective sensation of a palpable "afterglow" experienced following an important event. Studies performed by the Princeton PEAR team show that locations that have been the setting for intensely focused human activity (e.g., the King's Chamber of the Great Pyramid) retained some of that charge for long periods of time after the group activity had ceased (Nelson, Jahn, Dunne, Dobyns, & Bradish, 1998). Similarly, RNG recordings made off-season at the site of Boston Red Sox baseball games, and hours before a scheduled game, showed residual coherence above baseline, even when no people were present (Leskowitz, 2011).

A location thus affected is called a "conditioned space," and it can be created where human behavior and thought are consistent enough to create a vibrational imprint that affects subsequent biologic or biophysical activity in that immediate location. For example, the degree of acidity of a sample of purified neutral water can be influenced by placement in a laboratory setting that had been the site of prior regular group meditative activity; fairly rapid pH shifts of 1.0 international units were reported when test samples were moved into this space, even when such variables as temperature and atmospheric pressure were controlled (Tiller, Dibble, Nunley, & Shealy, 2004). These findings are reminiscent of Mesmer's technique of magnetizing samples of water to extend his healing influence for longer periods of time by taking advantage of the electromagnetic properties of water.

Future Directions

If in fact the shared attentional focus of sports fans can have a subtle energetic impact on their team, it should also be possible to maximize this effect by utilizing techniques such as guided imagery from the realm of hypnosis to optimize the fans' energetic cohesion, and hence their ability to resonantly create greater mind-body alignment in their players. Further research could study the degree to which performance is enhanced by coherent crowd energy; perhaps after singing the national anthem at the beginning of a game to ensure group entrainment, the fans could then be led en masse in a HeartMath exercise that directed their appreciative emotions toward the home team. The subjects of this experimental intervention, the home team, could of course not be blinded to the nature of the intervention, and so multiple trials would be necessary to rule out the possible contribution of many potential confounding variables. A nascent research base on distant group intentionality supports the theoretical validity of such an approach (McTaggart, 2007), and preliminary demonstrations of group intentionality in sports are in process (www.TheJoyOfSoxMovie.com/blog, March 21, 2009).

These same resonant processes would also be in effect in dyadic interactions like the therapist-patient relationship. Interpersonal emotional attunement and electromagnetic/energetic entrainment may also be among the "intangibles" that contribute to the success of some therapeutic encounters and the failure of others, whether or not classic verbally mediated hypnosis is directly involved (Feinstein, 2012). If the emotional context of the therapeutic encounter is one of appreciation, and if interactive heart coherent magnetic fields are thereby generated that can enhance mind-body coordination, then hypnotic phenomena may arise from this energetic interaction, along the lines of the specific verbal suggestions of the therapist. The dynamic interplay between verbal suggestions and energetic resonance in these encounters is worthy of further study, especially given the 200-year time lag since Mesmer's original demonstrations.

Several research studies could help prove or disprove the predictions of this resonant energy hypothesis:

1. Subjects in one-on-one or group-on-one interpersonal interactions could be electromagnetically isolated from the entraining group by sitting inside an insulated copper Faraday cage. All EMF effects would be neutralized, so a resonant impact would not be expected to occur.
2. Field RNG recordings could be made at a variety of high-intensity group events to extend the findings of the PEAR group by using the newer and more sensitive devices now available.
3. Athletes could have quantifiable performance skills tested in front of an appreciative audience, with the results compared to those obtained before a discordant audience. The model proposed here predicts enhanced performance before the appreciative audience.
4. Fans at an athletic event could be led in a pre-game heart coherence exercise, and resultant measurements made of such variables as RNG recordings, game outcomes, and subjective player responses. The impact of fan focus on the team as a whole versus on an individual player could also be tracked. These trained and energized fans would be predicted to have a greater

impact on dependent measures than chance alone.

5. Hypnotic susceptibility could be measured using validated instruments with subjects surrounded by appreciative witnesses versus critical or judgmental witnesses. Higher scores would be expected in the appreciative setting.

As this line of research continues to develop, we will better understand the intangible force of interpersonal resonance, a force that may explain how group attention can generate emergent transpersonal properties of human awareness and behavior.

References

Bair, C. (2008). The heart field effect: Synchronization of healer-subject heart rates in energy therapy. *Advances in Mind-Body Medicine, 23*(4), 10–19.

Begall, S., Cerveny, J., Neef, J., Vojtech, O., & Burda, H. (2008). Magnetic alignment in grazing and resting cattle and deer. *Proceedings of the National Academy of Sciences U S A, 105*(36), 13451–13455. doi:10.1073/pnas.0803650105

Cavagna, A., Cimarelli, A., Giardina, I., Parisi, G., Santagati, R., Stefanini, F., & Viale, M. (2010). Scale-free correlations in starling flocks. *Proceedings of the National Academy of Sciences U S A, 107*(26), 11865–11870. doi:10.1073/pnas.1005766107

Childre, D. & Martin, H. (1999). *The HeartMath solution: A revolutionary program for engaging the power of the heart's intelligence*. San Francisco, CA: HarperSanFrancisco.

Dossey, L. (2007). The PEAR Lab and nonlocal mind: Why they matter. *Explore: c 3*(3), 191–196.

Ehrenreich, B. (2006). *Dancing in the streets: A history of collective joy*. New York, NY: Metropolitan Books.

Ellenberger, H. (1970). *The discovery of the unconscious: The history and evolution of dynamic psychiatry.* New York, NY: Basic Books.

Feinstein, D. (2012). What does *energy* have to do with energy psychology? *Energy Psychology: Theory, Research, and Treatment, 4*(2), 59–80.

Gartzke, J. & Lange, K. (2002). Cellular target of weak magnetic fields: Ionic conduction along actin filaments in microvilli. *American Journal of Physiology and Cell Physiology, 283*(5), C1333–1346.

Gauld, A. (1992). *A history of hypnotism*. New York, NY: Cambridge University Press.

Giller, G. (2014). Salmon use magnetic field-based internal maps to find their way. *Scientific American,* February 7, 2014.

Green, E. (1992). Anomalous electrostatic phenomena in exceptional subjects. *Subtle Energies and Energy Medicine, 2*(3), 69–94.

Haker, H., Kawohl, W., Herwig, U., & Rössler, W. (2013). Mirror neuron activity in contagious yawning: An fMRI study. *Brain Imaging and Behavior, 7*(1), 28–34. doi:10.1007/s11682-012-9189-9

Jamieson, J. (2010). The home field advantage in athletics: A meta-analysis. *Journal of Applied Social Psychology, 40*(7), 1819–1842.

Kelly, S. F. (1993). The use of music as a hypnotic suggestion. *American Journal of Clinical Hypnosis, 36*(2), 83–90.

Leskowitz, E. (2009). The influence of group heart rhythm on target subject physiology. *Subtle Energies and Energy Medicine, 18*(3), 77–88.

Leskowitz, E. (2011). Random number generators at the ballpark: Preliminary evidence for the detection of moment-by-moment fluctuations in group attention as measured by Psigenics software. *International Journal of Healing and Caring, 11*(1), 1–11.

Leskowitz, E. (Producer) & Leskowitz, J. (Director). (2012). *The joy of Sox: Weird science and the power of intention* [Motion picture]. United States: 2 Cousins Productions and Pinch Hit Productions.

McCraty, R. (2004). The energetic heart: Bioelectromagnetic communication within and between people. In P. Rosch & M. Markov (Eds.), *Bioelectromagnetic medicine*. New York, NY: Marcel Dekker.

McCraty R., Atkinson M., & Bradley T. (2004). Electrophysiological evidence of intuition: The surprising role of the heart. *Journal of Alternative and Complementary Medicine, 10*(1), 133–143.

McTaggart, L. (2007). *The intention experiment: Using your thoughts to change your life and the world.* New York, NY: Free Press/Simon and Schuster.

Moss, P. & McEvedy, C. (1966). An epidemic of overbreathing among schoolgirls. *British Medical Journal, 2*(5525), 1295–1300.

Nelson R., Jahn, R. G., Dunne, B. J., Dobyns, Y. H. & Bradish, G. J. (2007). FieldREG II: Consciousness field effects: Replications and Explorations. *Explore: The Journal of Science and Healing, 3*(3), 279–293, 344.

Radin, D. (2006). *Entangled minds: Extrasensory experiences in a quantum reality*. New York, NY: Paraview Pocket Books.

Ravitz, L. (1959). Application of the electrodynamic field theory in biology, psychiatry, medicine, and hypnosis. *American Journal of Clinical Hypnosis, 1*(4), 135–150.

Schlitz, M., Vieten, C., & Miller, E. (2010). Worldview transformation and the development of social consciousness. *Journal of Consciousness Studies, 17*(7–8), 18–36.

Sheldrake, R. (1995). *The presence of the past: Morphic resonance and the habits of nature*. Rochester, VT: Park Street Press.

Shirer, W. (1941). *Berlin diary: The journal of a foreign correspondent, 1934–1941*. New York, NY: Alfred Knopf.

Tart, C. T. (1975). *States of consciousness.* El Cerrito, CA: Psychological Processes.

Tart, C. T. (2009). *The end of materialism: How evidence of the paranormal is bringing science and spirit together*. Oakland, CA: New Harbinger.

Tatum J. (1999). Clinical intuition and energy field resonance. In E. Leskowitz (Ed.), *Transpersonal hypnosis: Gateway to body mind and spirit*. Boca Raton, FL: CRC Press.

Tiller W., Dibble W., Nunley R., & Shealy, C. (2004). Toward general experimentation and discovery in conditioned laboratory spaces: Part I. Experimental pH change findings at some remote sites. *Journal of Alternative and Complementary Medicine, 10*(1), 145–157.

Tiller W., McCraty R., & Atkinson M. (1996). Cardiac coherence: A new, noninvasive measure of autonomic nervous system order. *Alternative Therapies in Health and Medicine, 2*(1), 52–65.

Walsh, R. & Vaughan, F. (Eds.). (1993). *Paths beyond ego: The transpersonal vision.* New York, NY: Tarcher/Putnam.

Watson, J. C., II & Krantz, A. J., III. (2003). Home field advantage: New stadium construction and team performance in professional sports. *Perceptual and Motor Skills, 97*(3 Pt 1), 794–796.

Wiltschko, R. & Wiltschko, W. (1995). *Magnetic orientation in animals.* Berlin, Germany: Springer.

Winter, A. (1998). *Mesmerized: Powers of mind in Victorian Britain.* Chicago, IL: University of Chicago Press.

Antifragile: Things That Gain from Disorder

Nassim Nicholas Taleb

Random House, 2014
Softcover, 544 pages
$17
ISBN: 978-0812979688

Reviewed by David Pierotti

Antifragile eloquently addresses one of the most prudent drivers of human and social behavior (that nearly everyone else is missing); namely, that when you add challenge to any system, it causes it to adapt, grow, and evolve. Taleb coined the term "antifragile" to describe those things that "thrive and grow when exposed to volatility, randomness, disorder, and stressors, and love adventure, risk, and uncertainty." Fragile, then, is the opposite: things or systems that fall apart or break when volatility is added. Somewhere in the middle of the two is robustness—the quality of a thing to "not mind" disorder—but the key difference in robustness is neither being harmed nor benefiting from the disorder.

Taleb goes to great lengths in describing how our modern society has become afraid of fragility. Our governments and so-called leaders have fashioned a modern overstructured world that suppresses randomness, and overprotects. Just as lying in bed 18 hours a day leads to muscle atrophy and bone loss, the denial and avoidance of the challenges of life makes humans and society en masse juvenilely dependent on those who do not deny and avoid.

Entrepreneurs are born out of hardship. Evolution occurs in the face of a threat to life. Children learn best when the material is harder than what they knew the day before. The examples go on and on, and can be found in all areas of life, from financial, social, business, and technology to relationship, education, and environmental systems.

The book gets off to a roaring start, seemingly promising a slew of examples of antifragility, but, disappointingly, takes a frightfully uninteresting philosophical/mathematical turn somewhere in the middle. Full of clumsy metaphors and uninteresting narratives, the book seems to be trying too hard to prove its own point. This could be a reflection of a personal bias—the fact that math doesn't excite me—but I found the philosophical/mathematical parts of the book less stimulating than those that bring theory to life with real-world examples.

That said, the adept reader can extract the message of *Antifragile,* which is: When a system is unable to bounce back from volatile circumstances, it is deemed fragile, like a coffee cup that is dropped from a height smashes. When a system can handle the volatility but does not benefit, it is robust, as a plastic cup will demonstrate. And when it is made better by hardship, it is termed antifragile, as most biological systems demonstrate.

What I do love about this book is its honesty. Taleb's dedication to the subject is obvious. His well-researched examples from many times and places in history take the reader on a valuable journey from naiveté to awareness. The awareness that what we believe to be safe and secure may just be the very thing primed to fail next. His life's work thus provides you with an insurance policy—a guarantee that if you follow the rules associated with the antifragile, you will flourish.

EMDR Toolbox: Theory and Treatment of Complex PTSD and Dissociation

Jim Knipe
Springer, 2014
Softcover, 272 pages
$65
ISBN: 978-0826171269

Reviewed by Esta Porter

EMDR Toolbox is written for clinicians who are knowledgeable in the basics of the Eye Movement Desensitization and Reprocessing (EMDR) protocol and are looking for skills, a toolbox, to enhance their clinical prowess with EMDR therapy. An EMDR Master clinician, Knipe has worked extensively with clients who suffer from complex trauma, which has a strongly negative impact on their well-being and many other aspects of their lives. In this population, getting to the root of the issues is often fairly difficult, as there are well-guarded behavioral manifestations that keep the client safe behind a coping wall. That wall, however, prevents the client from functioning as he or she desires professionally, personally, and interpersonally. The EMDR toolbox is a collection of tools for assisting the healing process of this most fragile of populations.

The book offers the clinical world adjunct techniques based in sound EMDR protocol to help clients move through their stuck points. It also provides insight into how these stuck points are constructed in the psyche, so that practitioners utilizing the methods covered have a clear understanding of how the blocks came to be.

Part I explains EMDR's Adaptive Information Processing (AIP) framework for treating complex PTSD. Part 2 details methods for resolving psychological defenses such as avoidance, idealization, and addictions. Part 3 presents information on treating dissociative personality structure. Knipe's basic framework for treating dissociative disorders includes the "loving eyes" process, which works with parts of a personality structure; treating defensive shame; and the Constant Installation of Present Orientation and Safety (CIPOS) procedure. Part IV gives case examples illustrating the tools in action. Throughout the book, Knipe provides both theory and documentation to support the use of the tools.

EMDR Toolbox represents a lifetime of experience, which Knipe graciously shares to the benefit of all clinicians.

Energy Makeover: A Conscious Way to Stay Young, Have More Fun, and Get More Done!

Betsy Muller

Motivational Press, 2011
Paperback, 215 pages
$19.95
ISBN: 978-1-935723-42-4

Reviewed by Carol Atkinson, PhD

At first glance, Betsy Muller's book *Energy Makeover* seemed like a weekend project that you could do yourself. Instead, Muller's book provides the reader a storehouse of energy altering modalities, modalities that Muller has practiced and refined. After finishing the book, I will forever equate Muller with heart massage. This massage (well worth the book's price) is profound and life altering. The book is written in such a way, however, that it comes across as a light-hearted sharing of Muller's process from left-brainer to healer and the healing practices she learned along the way. She's truly interested in sharing and helping others find their way out of the prison of their old, limited thinking.

A few of the modalities presented here include those that have been in the public eye for some time, such as EFT, Julie Cameron's *Artist's Way*, vision boards, and the Five Tibetans. Plus Muller shares some of her own customized processes, one called the Diamond Shield that helps you protect yourself from people who zap your energy. She also provides some alternatives to the traditional muscle testing techniques, which she believes are more reliable. At the end of her book, Muller provides the reader a self-assessment quiz that should be taken at the end of Chapter 1, as well as some EFT scripts that help us begin to break through issues such as weight, abundance, and creativity, among others.

Muller provides the framework for the modalities, and how she discovered them, through a retelling of her own experiences. Then she provides instruction on how to do these modalities that she has customized, with links to videos or other pertinent websites to help the reader "see" how these are done. As always, some modalities will resonate with the reader, while others may be tucked away for future use.

What is refreshing about the book is that Muller provides these modalities without drama, without any admonitions that these are the only way to change energy. She's clear that these modalities worked for her and people she's worked with over the years, but instead of asserting that there is just one way to clear the field, she provides numerous ways to get energy to change.

She mentions that the reader need not fear energy, that it is something that all of us can harness. When a person changes her mind, then immediately her emotions change. Once that occurs, then physical changes can begin. Thus energy modalities, when used with care, can help all of us find life more uplifting.

Psychic Psychology: Energy Skills for Life and Relationships

John Friedlander and Gloria Hemsher

North Atlantic Books, 2011
Softcover, 376 pages
$21.95
ISBN: 978-1556439971

Reviewed by Marilyn McWilliams

Psychic Psychology is a personal guidebook by the well-recognized psychic/writer team of John Friedlander and Gloria Hemsher. John Friedlander has degrees from Duke University and Harvard Law School, studied with Lewis Bostwick at the Berkley Psychic Institute, participated directly in the Seth class with channel Jane Roberts, and has been sharing this work since the 1970s. Gloria Hemsher, an intuitive since childhood and professional artist, joined John Friedlander in the late 1990s. They coauthored their first book, *Basic Psychic Development: A User's Guide to Auras, Chakras, and Clairvoyance,* in 1999. Today they teach workshops and intensives and, fortunately, have made the book *Psychic Psychology* available to the world.

Depending upon the reader's background and the time commitment the reader is willing to make, *Psychic Psychology* can be experienced as enjoyable introduction to psychic energy, a thought-provoking exploration of human energy and the role of desire in developing reliable happiness, or as a manual for a lifelong guided workshop with the authors. It is also excellent if one's only interest is in improving communication skills. There is something for everyone and a staggering amount available for readers ready and willing to absorb the entire package.

Part 1, "Psychic Skills for Life and Relationships," easily and comfortably provides even a beginner with critical energetic distinctions and techniques such as how to distinguish one's own energy from that of another and how to sort out and separate enmeshed energies. The authors follow the presentation of almost every concept with an experiential opportunity for the reader. Since there are nearly 100 such exercises, *Psychic Psychology* also earns it place on the bookshelf as a reference manual.

Part 1 continues with an impressive presentation of extremely useful distinctions and exercises on topics such as matching energies, exploding pictures, chakras, and the cultivation of neutrality. Chapter 6, "The Energy of Biological Differences: The Divine Complexity of Women, the Divine Simplicity of Men, and the Skills to Appreciate Both," includes detailed instructions on "Female Grounding" about which John Friedlander writes: "The women of my acquaintance find female grounding to be their most valuable tool." Care and management and understanding of the aura as our primary energetic indicator are main themes in the book. Chapter 6 continues: "Men's and women's auras are different in ways that affect how each gender engages the world and engages the other sex. Other things being equal, a woman's aura will be higher in frequency and about 2 feet larger in radius than a man's due to the energy that supports her ability to bear children." The information in Part 1 would justify a complete book in itself.

Part 2, "The Mysticism of Everyday Life," takes a different tone in that it draws heavily on author John Friedlander's studies with Seth. After the easy flow and readability of Part 1, readers who are unfamiliar with the teachings of Seth (and even some who are) may be slowed down by Part 2 as less penetrable or less applicable to daily life. Part 2 delves into more esoteric issues such as how one's individuality flows through eternity, multidimensional time, and explanations of why "both the ego and desire make profound and irreplaceable contributions to the meaning of our lives, even though rigidly pursuing the aims of either is unskillful and counterproductive."

After the somewhat arcane content of Part 2, the authors balance the obscure with the concrete. Part 3, aptly named "Practical Wisdom," focuses on communications or "conversations" with the world and every person, thing, and energy in it. It includes profound life lessons on the mechanics of anger, aura management, and difficult conversations. Again, the material offered here easily warrants a book of its own.

I recommend *Psychic Psychology* for those who enjoy having their reading flow interrupted by thoughts like "Wow, how did I get this far without knowing *that*?" The book draws from many teaching traditions and contains a remarkable number of important perspectives, many of which were new to me even after decades of interest and reading in the field. I particularly appreciate the down-to-earth explanations of the mechanics of developing our inherent psychic capabilities and the practical hands-on approach. The coauthors manage to deliver it all while demonstrating the same "fun, creativity, and playfulness" they recommend.

The authors write: "Engaging the chaotic, divine dance of life as fearlessly as you can, with kindness and generosity, promotes pleasure, generates happiness, and allows you to become ever more aware of the joy and meaning that are always and already fully present, yet miraculously and mysteriously, always growing." Then they provide the practical learning tools and exercises to actually do it.

God Is Not a Christian, nor a Jew, Muslim, Hindu: God Dwells with Us, in Us, around Us, as Us

Bishop Carlton Pearson

Atria Books, 2010
Paperback, 276 pages
$15.00
ISBN: 978-1-4165-8444-5

Reviewed by Charles B. Crenshaw Jr., MS

Bishop Carlton Pearson's book is at once earth shattering and enlightening, depending on your worldview. Here is a man who has forsaken all for the sake of the truth—in words from the book by which he has lived his life, "The truth will set you free." The author is clear about seeking the absolute truth.

In this mind-boggling work, he sets forth ideas like the "spiritual-industrial complex." The reference here reminds one of remarks made by President Eisenhower who warned that the United States should not go down the road of letting our capitalist ideology be the guide for taking us into war. Bishop Pearson has brought this understanding to the realm of his own background and has seen how megachurches, of which he was a pastor, are selling the social garb of religion to all comers and have moved away from the real truth of the spiritual life. This is a startling revelation from a man who was born into, in his own words, a fundamentalist Christian Pentecostal tradition.

When reading this text, the reader cannot help but ponder the fate of Bishop Pearson. He makes statements that smack of heresy (the word he uses). The reader will wonder if he even has a church to go to, whether there is a church anywhere in the United States that would accept him. Indeed he has found a place among free thinkers. He tells the story of the loss of his flock, not a major part of the text, but interesting to note how painful it was for him to come to the realizations that he did, and more noteworthy, to have the courage to act on his convictions. He does say that several people he talked to, in his past position, have come to the same conclusions, but because their livelihood depends on it, they don't have the courage of their convictions and continue on in the spiritual-industrial complex.

This book is sprinkled with Bishop Pearson's erudition. He goes to the roots of our understanding about religion and the words that we use or don't use related to it. He relays that one of the words used in the King James Version of the Bible for "religion" is "superstition." This, he says, is related to the fear, dread, or reverence the ancients had for demons or spirits. He leaves no stone unturned in his search for the truth and relates how indigenous African tradition impacted his own Pentecostal denomination, that is, that the denomination has roots in voodoo.

Some readers will find this book disgusting, and others will marvel at its frankness and the sheer courage it took for such a man to write it. It seems virtually impossible that someone like Bishop Carlton Pearson would have this change of mind, this change of heart. What brought on this current understanding in the autumn of his life? The thinking person will be astonished and ask, "How will the world be impacted by men and women like Bishop Carlton Pearson?"

Audacious Aging

Stephanie Marohn, Editor
Elite Books, 2009
Hardcover, 317 pages
$29.95
ISBN: 978-1-60070-061-3

Reviewed by Charles B. Crenshaw Jr., MS

Even the title of this book is presumptuous from the perspective of our youth-fixated society. Our society is always looking to remove something with Botox or smooth a line with the latest product to conceal the signs of aging. This book is the musings of lots of people, some famous and some not so famous. The stories range from a few pages (four or five) to 15 pages long and run the gambit of health tips to just pleasant thoughts about the process of aging.

This book is not just designed for baby boomers; it will be fascinating for anyone interested in the reality of the cycle of life. Having met several of the people in the book, reading their chapters was like having a quiet little talk with them about how they were getting along in their old age. Their viewpoints were different than I would have thought, which makes these audacious agers' comments even more fascinating. Even if the reader only knows the people by reputation or not at all, they will glean from this work wisdom about the way things were and how you might look at the aging process differently.

Lena Horne speaks about the powerful women who influenced her youth and led to her defiant response to societal conditions. The tips people like Andrew Weil, MD, offer are ones that any thinking individual would find useful as a guide for life in general, which leads to the point that all of life is about change. Like the lyric from a popular jazz song: "Everything must change, nothing stays the same/there are not many things in life you can be sure of/God lets the rain fall from the skies, sun light up the sky/everything must change," these brilliant people in this fascinating book help us to see just that in a classy and very readable way.

Free to Love, Free to Heal

David Simon, MD

Chopra Center Press, 2009
Hardcover, 191 pages
$22.95
ISBN: 978-0-9819640-0-3

Reviewed by Carol Crenshaw, EFT-INT

In *Free to Love, Free to Heal,* Dr. Simon uses physical maladies, negative emotions, and painful life situations as the starting point for deep and permanent healing. His method of getting to the core problem, traumas from the past that unconsciously influence us today, resonates with the EFT method of peeling away the layers of the onion to get to the core issue.

Dr. Simon is a board-certified neurologist and practitioner of yoga and meditation. Drawing from all aspects of his experience base, his step-by-step healing method weaves ancient Eastern wisdom with recent discoveries in Western neuroscience, psychology, and modern medicine. The case studies he offers reflect his vast experience base and understanding of the underlying causes of dis-ease. His basic theory is that dis-ease stems from "emotional malnourishment." Each of us has a story of why we can't give and receive love, or as he says, a "biography beneath the biology."

The good news is that once we can see our story, we are already on the path of healing and can proceed step by step to free ourselves and lead a richer, happier life. Regardless of the past, we can make new choices today, become responsible (which he spells "response-able"), and create a new and brighter future for ourselves.

Dr. Simon's holistic approach includes a systematic healing method, and incorporates yoga postures and breathing exercises for centeredness in going through the process. He also includes inspirational quotes, encouraging us to go within, from spiritual leaders such as the renowned Hindu sage Sri Ramakrishna, "Dwell, O mind, within yourself; enter no other's home. If you but seek there, you will find all you are searching for."

His process begins with identifying the emotional toxicity in our lives. How do we see ourselves and how did we form these beliefs? He calls these "core characteristics," which are similar to what we call in EFT "limiting beliefs." Rather than tapping as we do in EFT, he uses self-healing steps that engage us in various activities to bring themes to consciousness, release old beliefs, and replace them with healthier ones. This process includes identifying toxic traits, bringing your stories to light, noting where in the body you feel the emotions, noting the memories that go with the core feelings, and writing down your answers to six questions about painful experiences from the past. To release the pain, your stories need to be shared with a listening partner, real or imagined. Then there are rituals of release and forgiveness. What makes this process especially unique is his concept of "Healing to Awakening." Once we have healed ourselves and become whole again, then our task is to go beyond ourselves and be of service to others.

Who would I recommend this book to? I would recommend it to those who feel bound by a painful past and are ready to move on, those who have physical ailments, addiction challenges, anxiety or other emotional discomforts, those who want to work on healing themselves, those who want more love in their lives—in other words, just about all of us!

Faces of Combat, PTSD and TBI: One Journalist's Crusade to Improve Treatment for Our Veterans

Eric Newhouse

Issues Press, 2008
Softcover, 304 pages
$18.00
ISBN: 978-1930461062

Reviewed by Marilyn McWilliams

In *Faces of Combat, PTSD and TBI,* author Eric Newhouse delivers the breadth of view and clarity you might expect from a recipient of the 2000 Pulitzer Prize for Explanatory Reporting. The author is a veteran himself, and a self-described "crusading journalist." He writes *Psychology Today*'s blog "Invisible Wounds." Newhouse says, "As a journalist over the past four decades, I've tried to amplify the voices of those who usually go unheard so that the public and the policymakers understand what's happening to the people they don't see and to the people they're conditioned not to hear." He does that and more.

Part 1, "The Problem," presents a compelling combination of objective facts and subjective experiences of veterans. Newhouse dedicates Part 2, "The Solutions," to an exploration of practical action steps both for systems, using the progressive Montana VA as a model, and for individuals, by describing alternative drug-free treatments available outside of the VA. He concludes with a substantial list of resources.

True to its title, *Faces of Combat* humanizes the problems of the returning veteran with down-to-earth accounts of veterans' personal experiences, ranging from the internal struggles with flashbacks, rage, and nightmares to the more visible conditions of alcoholism, inability to hold a job, and homelessness. Newhouse examines the inordinately high rate of suicide and incarceration among the veteran population. He also explores systemic problems, such as veterans being directed by the military to seek help but being severely penalized when they do so, and the challenges of seeking help from the VA, which is overloaded and offers a narrow selection of treatments that, by virtually all measures, are inadequate.

Veterans themselves are the main characters in the true-life accounts, and Newhouse says he "spent days with many of them before they trusted me with their stories." Although the writing is clear and the veterans' stories are objectively presented, the book was not easy to read. *Faces of Combat, PTSD and TBI* is a crash course in the realities of war and the realities of society, both of which play a large role in a veteran's experience of PTSD (posttraumatic stress disorder) and the signature wound of the wars in Iraq and Afghanistan, TBI (traumatic brain injury). Even though I work with traumatized veterans, I found myself tapping on my collarbone as I read some of the painful descriptions, using a basic version of EFT (Emotional Freedom Techniques), which is one of the resources Newhouse describes in detail in the Solutions section. I found myself wondering if more readers would stay with the important material in the book if this simplified self-soothing technique were suggested to readers in the preface.

Just as the book's title is a clear sign of what's coming, however, the 21 chapters are descriptively titled and begin with concise recaps. The preface provides a clear road map of the book. Newhouse's own writing voice is readable and straightforward. An example from the preface: "It's not hopeless, but we do need to step up and decide to take care of our veterans." In his conclusion, he addresses the economics of the war and notes: "That's a deep hole, and it reminds me of the wisdom of the First Law of Holes: 'When you're in a hole, quit digging.'"

Eric Newhouse systematically exposes the problems faced by returning veterans and puts real-life "Faces" of veterans onto those challenges. He lays out the shortcomings of the current systems, explores what is being done and what can be done, then finishes his concluding chapter with five major recommendations. He doesn't argue that the solutions are easy, only that they are necessary both for our veterans and for our country, and he welcomes alternative and additional ideas.

I recommend this book to any counselor, employer, family member, or friend of a veteran who wants to understand the veteran's world, as well as to veterans themselves who need to know that they are not alone. It should be required reading for our military command, for every member of Congress, and for VA staff, starting with the Secretary of the VA.

Healing the Heart of the World: Harnessing the Power of Intention to Change Your Life and Your Planet

Dawson Church, PhD, Editor
Elite Books, 2005
Hardcover, 391 pages
$24.95
ISBN: 978-0971088856

Reviewed by Carol Crenshaw, EFT-INT

It doesn't take much today to be aware of the intense suffering and destruction going on everywhere on planet Earth. At times it can be acutely discouraging and totally overwhelming. Where do we start to make a change and bring more light into our lives and the lives of others? *Healing the Heart of the World* is a book that gives us hope, direction, and a fresh, invigorating perspective.

Today's noted visionaries, activists, and authors in many fields share their experiences and views on how all of us can make a difference. They all come to the same conclusions, whether they are speaking about creating authentic community, empowering the feminine, exploring our interior spiritual realms, messages in water, communing with nature, or expressing wisdom in work. The common themes that emerge from all these perspectives include: Love is the healer, forgiveness and gratitude are needed to move forward, life is about relationships, helping others starts with knowing the self, spirituality in action creates change, transformation requires stepping back from busy-ness, and, most of all, small acts go a long way. All conclude that the time is now for change to take place. As Anodea Judith states, "Highly powerful but still immature, we stand poised between epic creation and potential annihilation, equally capable of either."

Many of the authors agree that seeing ourselves in others and others in ourselves allows us to feel the suffering of others as our own suffering, to experience the oneness of all creation. Neale Donald Walsch states it succinctly, "The type of behavior we see in the headlines every day could only be produced by an idea that we are not intrinsically connected, but rather separate from each other, and, therefore, dependent on ourselves alone for our survival." When we think universally, we also more easily take responsibility for ourselves, letting go of any harm or injustice that's been done to us. Our focus goes beyond our limited self.

One of the strongest themes running through the book is that we are spiritual beings first, capable of using our spiritual energy for creative acts, transformative acts, visionary acts. Starting by knowing the Self and working outward, we have tremendous power to change the world. This includes every single person, acting in small ways every day to reach out to others and stay connected with people, nature, and our divine Self. Little everyday acts of kindness and connectedness add up to enormous changes. In Masaru Emoto's experiments with water, he found that words like "Love," "Thanks," and "Wisdom" created beautiful crystals in water, while words like "You make me sick" produced incomplete crystals or no crystals at all. Our words do make a difference.

I invite you to turn to any chapter in this comprehensive work to find something simple you can do right now, a tip for moving your mind in a different direction, or a piece of information that connects the dots for you.

The Heart of Healing: Inspired Ideas, Wisdom and Comfort from Today's Leading Voices

Dawson Church, Editor

Elite Books, 2004
Hardcover, 327 pages
$25
ISBN: 978-0972002837

Reviewed by Lucie Monroe, EFT INT-1

This ambitious book gathers 31 articles by as many healing arts practitioners from diverse backgrounds. Here, established and respected medical doctors, neurologists, chiropractors, psychologists, counselors, shamans, spiritual and energy healers, and coaches, among others, share their ideas about the nature of health and the healing process. Their reflections are organized along six different axes: reclaiming the soul in healing, sexual healing, the absence of disease versus vibrant health, healing and consciousness, ancient new approaches to healing, and the future of healing. Although each individual article provides interesting and even profound insights into one or several facets of *The Heart of Healing,* there isn't much cohesion between the different chapters. The whole appears fragmented, if not contrived. But this should come as no surprise when attempting to define such a multidimensional topic.

A review of select CAM modalities for the prevention and treatment of PTSD

Lake, J. (2014). A review of select CAM modalities for the prevention and treatment of PTSD. *Psychiatric Times,* July 25, 2014. Retrieved from http://www.psychiatrictimes.com/integrative-psychiatry/review-select-cam-modalities-prevention-and-treatment-ptsd

Abstract

The personal, social, and economic burdens of human suffering related to PTSD are major issues facing society. Conventional pharmacotherapy and psychotherapy reduce the severity of some PTSD symptoms; however, their effectiveness is limited, and many patients discontinue these pharmacological and psychotherapeutic treatments before achieving full remission. The limited effectiveness of conventional approaches and unmet treatment needs of patients provide compelling arguments for effective conventional and complementary and alternative medicine (CAM) interventions aimed at preventing PTSD and treating chronic PTSD.

Amnesia for early life stress does not preclude the adult development of posttraumatic stress disorder symptoms in rats

Poulos, A. M., Reger, M., Mehta, N., Zhuravka, I., Sterlace, S. S., Gannam, C., ... Fanselow, M. S. (2014). Amnesia for early life stress does not preclude the adult development of posttraumatic stress disorder symptoms in rats. *Biological Psychiatry, 76*(4), 306–314. doi:10.1016/j.biopsych.2013.10.007

Abstract

Background: Traumatic experience can result in lifelong changes in the ability to cope with future stressors and emotionally salient events. These experiences, particularly during early development, are a significant risk factor for later life anxiety disorders such as posttraumatic stress disorder (PTSD). However, because traumatic experience typically results in strong episodic memories, it is not known whether such long-term memories are necessary for particular features of PTSD, such as enhanced fear and anxiety. Here, we used a fear conditioning procedure in juvenile rats before maturation of the neural systems supporting declarative memory to assess the necessity of early memory to the later life development of PTSD-related symptoms.

Methods: Nineteen-day old rats were exposed to unpredictable and inescapable footshocks, and fear memory for the shock context was assessed during adulthood. Thereafter, adult animals were either exposed to single-trial fear conditioning or elevated plus maze or sacrificed for basal diurnal corticosterone and quantification of neuronal glucocorticoid and neuropeptide Y receptors.

Results: Early trauma exposed rats displayed stereotypic footshock reactivity, yet by adulthood, hippocampus-dependent contextual fear-related memory was absent. However, adult rats showed sensitized fear learning, aberrant basal circadian fluctuations of corticosterone, increased amygdalar glucocorticoid receptors, decreased time spent in the open arm of an elevated plus maze, and an odor aversion associated with early-life footshocks.

Conclusions: These results suggest that traumatic experience during developmental periods of hippocampal immaturity can promote lifelong changes in symptoms and neuropathology associated with human PTSD, even if there is no explicit memory of the early trauma.

Spontaneous brain activity in combat related PTSD

Yan, X., Brown, A. D., Lazar, M., Cressman, V. L., Henn-Haase, C., Neylan, T. C., ... Marmar, C. R. (2013). Spontaneous brain activity in combat related PTSD. *Neuroscience Letters, 547*, 1–5. doi:10.1016/j.neulet.2013.04.032

Abstract

Posttraumatic stress disorder (PTSD) is a prevalent psychiatric disorder, especially in combat veterans. Existing functional neuroimaging studies have provided important insights into the neural mechanisms of PTSD using various experimental paradigms involving trauma recollection or other forms of emotion provocation. However, it is not clear whether the abnormal brain activity is specific to the mental processes related to the experimental tasks or reflects general patterns across different brain states. Thus, studying intrinsic spontaneous brain activity without the influence of external tasks may provide valuable alternative perspectives to further understand the neural characteristics of PTSD. The present study evaluated the magnitudes of spontaneous brain activity of male U.S. veterans with or without PTSD, with the two groups matched on age, gender, and ethnicity. Amplitudes of low-frequency fluctuation (ALFF), a data-driven analysis method, were calculated on each voxel of the resting state fMRI data to measure the magnitudes of spontaneous brain activity. Results revealed that PTSD subjects showed increased spontaneous activity in the amygdala, ventral anterior cingulate cortex, insula, and orbital frontal cortex, as well as decreased spontaneous activity in the precuneus, dorsal lateral prefrontal cortex, and thalamus. Within the PTSD group, larger magnitudes of spontaneous activity in the thalamus, precuneus, and dorsal lateral prefrontal cortex were associated with lower reexperiencing symptoms. Comparing our results with previous functional neuroimaging findings, increased activity of the amygdala and anterior insula and decreased activity of the thalamus are consistent patterns across emotion provocation states and the resting state.

PTSD and gene variants: New pathways and new thinking

Skelton, K., Ressler, K. J., Norrholm, S. D., Jovanovic, T., & Bradley-Davino, B. (2012). PTSD and gene variants: New pathways and new thinking. *Neuropharmacology, 62*(2), 628–637. doi:10.1016/j.neuropharm.2011.02.013

Abstract

Posttraumatic Stress disorder (PTSD) is an anxiety disorder that can develop as a result of exposure to a traumatic event and is associated with significant functional impairment. Family and twin studies have found that risk for PTSD is associated with an underlying genetic vulnerability and that more than 30% of the variance associated with PTSD is related to a heritable component. Using a fear-conditioning model to conceptualize the neurobiology of PTSD, three primary neuronal systems have been investigated: the hypothalamic-pituitary-adrenal axis, the locus coeruleus-noradrenergic system, and neurocircuitry interconnecting the limbic system and frontal cortex. The majority of the initial investigations into main effects of candidate genes hypothesized to be associated with PTSD risk have been negative, but studies examining the interaction of genetic polymorphisms with specific environments in predicting PTSD have produced several positive results that have increased our understanding of the determinants of risk and resilience in the aftermath of trauma. Promising avenues of inquiry into the role of epigenetic modification have also been proposed to explain the enduring impact of environmental exposures that occur during key, often early, developmental periods on gene expression. Studies of PTSD endophenotypes, which are heritable biomarkers associated with a circumscribed trait within the more complex psychiatric disorder, may be more directly amenable to analysis of the underlying genetics and neural pathways and have provided promising targets for elucidating the neurobiology of PTSD. Knowledge of the genetic underpinnings and neuronal pathways involved in the etiology and maintenance of PTSD will allow for improved targeting of primary prevention amongst vulnerable individuals or populations, as well as timely, targeted treatment interventions.

Abnormal baseline brain activity in posttraumatic stress disorder: A resting-state functional magnetic resonance imaging study

Yin, Y., Li, L., Jin, C., Hu, X., Duan, L., Eyler, L. T., ... & Li, W. (2011). Abnormal baselinc brain activity in posttraumatic stress disorder: A resting-state functional magnetic resonance imaging study. *Neuroscience Letters, 498*(3), 185–189. doi:10.1016/j.neulet.2011.02.069

Abstract

Little is known about how spontaneous brain activity during the resting state may be altered in posttraumatic stress disorder (PTSD) compared to traumatized individuals. In the current study, we used a measure of amplitude of low-frequency (0.01–0.08 Hz) fluctuation (ALFF) to investigate the regional baseline brain function of this disorder. Fifty-four medication-naive PTSD patients and 72 matched traumatized comparison subjects who experienced the Sichuan major earthquake participated in a functional magnetic resonance imaging (fMRI) scan. We analyzed the difference between the PTSD and comparison groups during a resting state using ALFF. PTSD patients showed decreased ALFF values in right lingual gyrus, cuneus, middle occipital gyrus, insula, and cerebellum, and increased ALFF values in right medial and middle frontal gyri, relative to traumatized individuals without PTSD. The ALFF value in the right medial frontal gyrus was positively correlated with severity of the disorder. Our findings show that abnormality of intrinsic brain activity exists under resting conditions in PTSD patients exposed to a major earthquake. Altered ALFF in predominantly right hemisphere cortical and subcortical regions and in cerebellum potentially contributes to the neural mechanisms underlying traumatic memory and symptoms in PTSD.

Altered processing of contextual information during fear extinction in PTSD: An fMRI study

Rougemont Bücking, A., Linnman, C., Zeffiro, T. A., Zeidan, M. A., Lebron Milad, K., Rodriguez Romaguera, J., ... & Milad, M. R. (2011). Altered processing of contextual information during fear extinction in PTSD: An fMRI study. *CNS Neuroscience and Therapeutics, 17*(4), 227–236. doi:10.1111/j.1755-5949.2010.00152.x

Abstract

Medial prefrontal cortical areas have been hypothesized to underlie altered contextual processing in posttraumatic stress disorder (PTSD). We investigated brain signaling of contextual information in this disorder. Eighteen PTSD subjects and 16 healthy trauma-exposed subjects underwent a two-day fear conditioning and extinction paradigm. On day 1, within visual context A, a conditioned stimulus (CS) was followed 60% of the time by an electric shock (conditioning). The conditioned response was then extinguished (extinction learning) in context B. On day 2, recall of the extinction memory was tested in context B. Skin conductance response (SCR) and functional magnetic resonance imaging (fMRI) data were collected during context presentations. There were no SCR group differences in any context presentation. Concerning fMRI data, during late conditioning, when context A signaled danger, PTSD subjects showed dorsal anterior cingulate cortical (dACC) hyperactivation. During early extinction, when context B had not yet fully acquired signal value for safety, PTSD subjects still showed dACC hyperactivation. During late extinction, when context B had come to signal safety, they showed ventromedial prefrontal cortex (vmPFC) hypoactivation. During early extinction recall, when context B signaled safety, they showed both vmPFC hypoactivation and dACC hyperactivation. These findings suggest that PTSD subjects show alterations in the processing of contextual information related to danger and safety. This impairment is manifest even prior to a physiologically measured, cue-elicited fear response, and characterized by hypoactivation in vmPFC and hyperactivation in dACC.

Common genetic liability to major depression and posttraumatic stress disorder in men

Koenen, K. C., Fu, Q. J., Ertel, K., Lyons, M. J., Eisen, S. A., True, W. R., Goldberg, J., & Tsuang, M. T. (2008). Common genetic liability to major depression and posttraumatic stress disorder in men. *Journal of Affective Disorders, 105*(1–3), 109–115. doi:10.1016/j.jad.2007.04.021

Abstract

Background: Major depression (MD) and posttraumatic stress disorder (PTSD) are highly comorbid. The degree to which a common genetic liability explains the etiology of the MD-PTSD association has not been quantified and has important implications for research and prevention.

Methods: This paper presents an analysis of data from 6,744 members of the Vietnam Era Twin Registry. MD and PTSD were assessed using the Diagnostic Interview Schedule-III-R in 1991–92. Bivariate twin modeling was conducted to determine the genetic and environmental etiology of the MD-PTSD association.

Results: The best-fitting model for the MD-PTSD association included a substantial genetic correlation($r = .77$; 95% CI, .50–1.00) and a modest individual-specific environmental correlation($r = .34$; 95% CI, .19–.48). Common genetic liability explained 62.5% of MD-PTSD comorbidity. Genetic influences common to MD explained 15% of the total variance in risk for PTSD and 58% of the genetic variance in PTSD. Individual-specific environmental influences common to MD explained only 11% of the individual-specific environmental variance in PTSD.

Limitations: Our participants were male Vietnam era veterans and our findings may not generalize to civilians, females, or other cohorts.

Conclusions: MD–PTSD comorbidity is largely explained by common genetic influences. Substantial genetic overlap between MD and PTSD implies that genes implicated in the etiology of MD are strong candidates for PTSD and vice versa. Environmental influences on MD and PTSD explain less of their covariation and appear to be largely disorder-specific. Research is needed to identify environmental factors that influence the development of MD versus PTSD in the context of common genetic liability.

A feasibility study: Emotional Freedom Techniques for depression in Australian adults

Stapleton, P., Devine, S., Chatwin, H., Porter, B., & Sheldon, T. (2014). A feasibility study: Emotional Freedom Techniques for depression in Australian adults. *Current Research in Psychology, 5*(1), 19–33. doi:10.3844/crpsp.2014.19.33

Abstract

The purpose of this study was to investigate the feasibility of using Clinical Emotional Freedom Techniques (EFT) to treat Major Depressive Disorder in an adult population by way of a therapeutic group setting. Adults were assigned to EFT group treatment for a period of 8 weeks. Diagnostic assessment was completed immediately pre and post treatment using the Mini International Neuropsychiatric Interview. In addition to this, self-report assessments measuring symptomatic evidence of depression were completed by the participants before the treatment, after the treatment, and at 3-month follow-up. Comparisons with a community group were made at pre and post intervention and 3-month follow-up. The results indicated a change in diagnosis in each of the participants, with data indicating an overall improvement for the treatment group for depressive symptoms. Study implications and limitations are discussed.

No health without mental health

Prince, M., Patel, V., Saxena, S., Maj, M., Maselko, J., Phillips, M. R., & Rahman, A. (2007). No health without mental health. *Lancet, 370*(9590), 859–877. doi:10.1016/S0140-6736(07)61238-0

Summary

About 14% of the global burden of disease has been attributed to neuropsychiatric disorders, mostly due to the chronically disabling nature of depression and other common mental disorders, alcohol-use and substance-use disorders, and psychoses. Such estimates have drawn attention to the importance of mental disorders for public health. However, because they stress the separate contributions of mental and physical disorders to disability and mortality, they might have entrenched the alienation of mental health from mainstream efforts to improve health and reduce poverty. The burden of mental disorders is likely to have been underestimated because of inadequate appreciation of the connectedness between mental illness and other health conditions. Because these interactions are protean, there can be no health without mental health. Mental disorders increase risk for communicable and non-communicable diseases, and contribute to unintentional and intentional injury. Conversely, many health conditions increase the risk for mental disorder, and comorbidity complicates help-seeking, diagnosis, and treatment, and influences prognosis. Health services are not provided equitably to people with mental disorders, and the quality of care for both mental and physical health conditions for these people could be improved. We need to develop and evaluate psychosocial interventions that can be integrated into management of communicable and non-communicable diseases. Health-care systems should be strengthened to improve delivery of mental health care, by focusing on existing programs and activities, such as those that address the prevention and treatment of HIV, tuberculosis, and malaria; gender-based violence; antenatal care; integrated management of childhood illnesses and child nutrition; and innovative management of chronic disease. An explicit mental health budget might need to be allocated for such activities. Mental health affects progress toward the achievement of several Millennium Development Goals, such as promotion of gender equality and empowerment of women, reduction of child mortality, improvement of maternal health, and reversal of the spread of HIV/AIDS. Mental health awareness needs to be integrated into all aspects of health and social policy, health-system planning, and delivery of primary and secondary general health care.

The role of genetic variation in the causation of mental illness: An evolution-informed framework

Uher, R. (2009). The role of genetic variation in the causation of mental illness: An evolution-informed framework. *Molecular Psychiatry, 14*, 1072–1082. doi:10.1038/mp.2009.85

Abstract

The apparently large genetic contribution to the aetiology of mental illness presents a formidable puzzle. Unlike common physical disorders, mental illness usually has an onset early in the reproductive age and is associated with substantial reproductive disadvantage. Therefore, genetic variants associated with vulnerability to mental illness should be under strong negative selection pressure and be eliminated from the genetic pool through natural selection. Still, mental disorders are common and twin studies indicate a strong genetic contribution to their aetiology. Several theories have been advanced to explain the paradox of high heritability and reproductive disadvantage associated with the same common phenotype, but none provides a satisfactory explanation for all types of mental illness. At the same time, identification of the molecular substrate underlying the large genetic contribution to the aetiology of mental illness is proving more difficult than expected. The quest for genetic variants associated with vulnerability to mental illness is predicated upon the common disease/common variant (CDCV) hypothesis. On the basis of a summary of evidence, it is concluded that the CDCV hypothesis is untenable for most types of mental illness. An alternative evolution-informed framework is proposed, which suggests that gene-environment interactions and rare genetic variants constitute most of the genetic contribution to mental illness. Common mental illness with mild reproductive disadvantage is likely to have a large contribution from interactions between common genetic variants and environmental exposures. Severe mental illness that confers strong reproductive disadvantage is likely to have a large and pleiotropic contribution from rare variants of recent origin. This framework points to a need for a paradigm change in genetic research to enable major progress in elucidating the aetiology of mental illness.

Tapping for PEAS: Emotional Freedom Technique (EFT) in reducing Presentation Expression Anxiety Syndrome (PEAS) in university students

Boath, E., Stewart, A., & Carryer, A. (2012). Tapping for PEAS: Emotional Freedom Technique (EFT) in reducing Presentation Expression Anxiety Syndrome (PEAS) in university students. *Innovative Practice in Higher Education, 1*(2).

Abstract

Presentation anxiety is one of the most common fears that people express. Emotional Freedom Technique (EFT), which is also known as tapping, is an emerging complementary therapy that has been used to treat a variety of phobias. Participants were a convenience sample of 25 third-year Foundation Degree level complementary therapy students undertaking a research module. The module included an assessed presentation, which was known to generate anxiety among students. The students were given a 15-minute assignment workshop. They then received a 15-minute lecture introducing EFT and were then guided though one round of EFT focusing on their fear of public speaking. The students were assessed using the Subjective Units of Distress (SUD) scale and the Hospital Anxiety and Depression (HAD) scale pre and post EFT. Immediately following their presentation, the students were invited to take part in a brief face-to-face interview to explore their use of and feelings about EFT. Twenty-one of the total sample of 25 students (84%) participated in the research. There was a significant reduction in SUD (p = 0.002), HAD (p = 0.048) and HAD Anxiety Subscale (p = 0.037). There was no difference in the HAD Depression Subscale (p = 0.719). The qualitative data were analyzed using a framework approach that revealed three themes: nerves, novelty, and the practical application of EFT. Despite the limitations of the study, the results suggest that EFT may be a useful addition to curricula for courses that include oral presentations.

Emotional freedom technique: Energy psychology integration in the workplace setting

Scott, J. (2008). Emotional freedom technique: Energy psychology integration in the workplace setting. *Counselling at Work,* Winter 2008/9, 9–12.

Abstract

This article discusses the application of one of the energy psychology (EP) methods, emotional freedom technique (EFT), in the workplace setting. As the trauma support group manager for trains, working in the London Underground counselling and trauma service, I have integrated EFT into my counselling practice with traumatized members of Transport for London (TfL), trauma volunteer training, support of colleagues in the workplace, and my own self-support and self-supervision processes. My interest in EFT developed through my wish to understand and learn an approach that appeared to offer a simple and effective way of reducing the impact of pain, distress, and trauma on individuals.

I found the technique to be easy to learn and teach, and easy to apply. For those individuals who like EFT, it can be experienced as life changing. In this article, I draw on examples of EFT application in a variety of situations.

Nanoparticles for tracing acupuncture meridians and Bonghan ducts

Johng, H.-M., Lee, C.-H., Yoo, J. S., Yoon, T.-J., Shin, H.-S., Lee, B.-C., ... Soh, K.-S. (2006). Nanoparticles for tracing acupuncture meridians and Bonghan ducts. In S. I. Kim & T. S. Suh (Eds.), *World Congress on Medical Physics and Biomedical Engineering 2006 (IFMBE Proceedings,* Vol. 14, pp. 3584–3586). Berlin, Germany: Springer.

Abstract

Nanoparticles are increasingly used in various fields, especially in biomedical research such as enzyme immobilization, contrast enhancing media, and imaging of cellular and molecular structures. We report on the use of fluorescent magnetic nanoparticles for tracing acupuncture meridians and their anatomical structures, that is, Bonghan ducts. By injecting nanoparticles into the acupuncture points (LR9) of mice, we observed them at other acupoints (LR3) of the same liver meridian, which implied the propagation of nanoparticles along the meridian. Another use of nanoparticles was injecting them into a Bonghan corpuscle and observing them to flow along the Bonghan duct on the surface of mammalian internal organs. The third application was injecting them into lymph nodes so that Bonghan ducts inside lymphatic vessels were detected and visualized by the fluorescence of nanoparticles. Confocal laser scanning microscope images of cryo-sectioned specimens showed that the nanoparticles were preferentially taken up by Bonghan ducts. Transmission electron microscope images revealed the nanoparticles captured in the extra cellular matrix of Bonghan ducts.

Blinded with science: Trivial graphs and formulas increase ad persuasiveness and belief in product efficacy

Tal, A., & Wansink, B. (2014). Blinded with science: Trivial graphs and formulas increase ad persuasiveness and belief in product efficacy. *Public Understanding of Science,* October 15, 2014. doi:10.1177/0963662514549688

Abstract

The appearance of being scientific can increase persuasiveness. Even trivial cues can create such an appearance of a scientific basis. In our studies, including simple elements, such as graphs (Studies 1–2) or a chemical formula (Study 3), increased belief in a medication's efficacy. This appears to be due to the association of such elements with science, rather than increased comprehensibility, use of visuals, or recall. Belief in science moderates the persuasive effect of graphs, such that people who have a greater belief in science are more affected by the presence of graphs (Study 2). Overall, the studies contribute to past research by demonstrating that even trivial elements can increase public persuasion despite their not truly indicating scientific expertise or objective support.

Psychological determinants of consumer acceptance of personalised nutrition in 9 European countries

Poínhos, R., van der Lans, I. A., Rankin, A., Fischer, A. R. H., Bunting, B., Kuznesof, S., Stewart-Knox, B., & Frewer, L. J. (2014). Psychological determinants of consumer acceptance of personalised nutrition in 9 European countries. *PLoS One, 9*(10), e110614. doi:10.1371/journal.pone.0110614

Abstract

Objective: To develop a model of the psychological factors that predict people's intention to adopt personalized nutrition. Potential determinants of adoption included perceived risk and benefit, perceived self-efficacy, internal locus of control, and health commitment.

Methods: A questionnaire, developed from exploratory study data and the existing theoretical literature, and including validated psychological scales, was administered to $N = 9381$ participants from nine European countries (Germany, Greece, Ireland, Poland, Portugal, Spain, the Netherlands, the UK, and Norway).

Results: Structural equation modeling indicated that the greater participants' perceived benefits to be associated with personalized nutrition, the more positive their attitudes were towards personalized nutrition, and the greater their intention to adopt it. Higher levels of nutrition self-efficacy were related to more positive attitudes toward, and a greater expressed intention to adopt, personalized nutrition. Other constructs positively impacting attitudes toward personalized nutrition included more positive perceptions of the efficacy of regulatory control to protect consumers (e.g., in relation to personal data protection), higher self-reported internal health locus of control, and health commitment. Although higher perceived risk had a negative relationship with attitude and an inverse relationship with perceived benefit, its effects on attitude and intention to adopt personalized nutrition were less influential than perceived benefit. The model was stable across the different European countries, suggesting that psychological factors determining adoption of personalized nutrition have generic applicability across different European countries.

Conclusion: The results suggest that transparent provision of information about potential benefits and protection of consumers' personal data are important for adoption, delivery of public health benefits, and commercialization of personalized nutrition.

EP Research Symposium 2015: Call for Papers

The Association for Comprehensive Energy Psychology will be hosting its Fifth Annual Research Symposium next year. To this end, we are accepting research papers in the fields of Energy Psychology and Energy Medicine to be presented at our international conference on Thursday, May 29, 2015, in Reston, VA.

We are seeking original empirical research, clinical single subject case studies, experimental design studies, randomized controlled studies, and theoretical and review papers. New researchers and graduate students are especially encouraged to present. The deadline for submissions is November 20, 2014.

Notification of accepted papers will be made by January 15, 2015.

For further details, see: http://www.energypsych.org/?page=call_for_papers
Please send submissions to: John Freedom, Chair, ACEP Research Committee
research_committee@energypsych.org.

CPSIA information can be obtained
at www.ICGtesting.com
Printed in the USA
FSOW02n0315210115
4618FS

9 781604 151305